The Pivot fc Educators: ADHD/Autism

How Looking Through a Different Lens at the Neurodivergent Mind Can Change Our Thoughts and Feelings About a Diagnosis

Kim Gallo, M.S. CCC-SLP

To my daughter Kayle

Always know you are loved

Table of Contents

About the Author

While earning a bachelor's degree in Psychology in the late 90s, Kim Gallo worked alongside Certified Behavior Analysts teaching young toddlers who were newly diagnosed with autism. She then earned Board Certification as an Associate Behavior Analyst. In 2004, Kim earned a Master's degree in Speech-Language Pathology, and in 2005, she completed her fellowship and earned her Certificate of Clinical Competence (CCC), thus becoming certified by the American Speech and Hearing Association. She has worked in various settings on multidisciplinary teams with the Early Intervention program, in K-12 schools, as well as in private practice with both children and young adults. Kim is also the parent of two children, one of whom is a neurodivergent young adult.

Introduction

In the late 90s, I answered an advertisement on a college bulletin board. It was for a position as a tutor or trainer for a toddler diagnosed with autism. It said, "No experience is necessary. Will train!"

I interviewed, and I went on to be "hired" by that family for that position. I was trained by a Behavior Analyst to provide Applied Behavior Analysis therapy or, as it was called at the time, discrete trial therapy. Through that family, I met several other families looking for help with their ABA-home program. These opportunities changed the trajectory of my life. I went on to earn a bachelor's degree in psychology and later became a Board-Certified Associate Behavior Analyst. Many families I worked with at the time worked with the same Speech-Language Pathologist, Donna W. On many occasions, I had the opportunity to accompany these students to speech therapy. Meeting Donna W. each week and watching her in therapy working with kids has also changed my life.

A few years later, I enrolled in graduate school to become a Speech-Language Pathologist. I was lucky enough to complete my internship alongside my mentor, Donna W. Much of her private practice was dedicated to helping families with autistic kids learn how to communicate and develop social skills. Around the same time, I gave birth to my first child, my daughter Kayle. Kayle appeared to be "typically developing" in her early years. She was bright, chatty, theatrical, and resilient. She was also disorganized and short-tempered, and she struggled to follow directions more and more as she grew.

In October, when she was eight years old and in the third grade, we decided to take a family trip to the local pumpkin patch. It was a day I'll never forget. It should have been a fun yet ordinary day. But we all left feeling upset, and at the time, Kayle, her brother, and I all cried at some point on this day. What happened? Nothing really, but everything was a challenge for Kayle. She just never seemed to listen, from getting out of the car to asking her to hold my hand or stay near me, to not touch everything, to leave her brother alone, to ask her to try to be quiet when adults were talking. Next thing you know, my husband is cranky, my three-year-old son is fussy, and I am over-the-top frustrated, trying my hardest to satisfy everyone while keeping the kids safe. So, what should have been a pleasant fall outing for a family of four turned into complete misery.

Upon arriving home that day, I remember crying in the bathroom, wondering where I was going wrong. I had a smart, healthy, "normal" kid. Why was she so defiant? So strong-willed? Remember, I was a Behaviorist and a Speech-Language Pathologist. Why were none of the tools in my toolbox working here? I tried positive and negative reinforcement. I tried token economies. I tried positive and negative punishment, small rewards, big rewards, anything and everything. Nothing worked. I was starting to feel like Kayle was doing *this* to me on purpose—something spiteful—but I knew in my heart that that didn't make sense.

I called my old friend Donna W. on that day from the floor of my bathroom. I just wanted to be consoled, but what I got was so much more. Donna suggested that what I was describing did not sound like it was in Kayle's control. I was shocked and a little relieved at the idea that this thing going on with Kayle could potentially not be anyone's fault or in anyone's control. Soon after that conversation, I brought her in for some psycho-educational testing, and she received the diagnosis of ADHD. Today, Kayle is a young woman. She earned a college degree at that same school where I saw that advertisement on the bulletin board in the late 90s.

She has a job, she has friends, and she is an athlete who swam on a nationally-ranked Synchronized Swim team for over a decade. While she still has challenges and struggles related to her diagnosis, finding out about that diagnosis, as well as my mindset regarding that diagnosis, has changed our lives. Reflecting on that day, I realize how grateful I am for my friendship with Donna and for Kayle's diagnosis. It allowed me to feel differently about Kayle. I was angry and frustrated much of the time when we were together back then. Knowing that she is neurodivergent allows me to pivot my perspective about what I expect, how I think, what I think, and how I teach and parent. This experience, along with over 20 years of working with neurodivergent individuals, has led me to want to share some of my knowledge and information with you. I know our children are likely quite different, but I hope that after reading this book, you will have a pivot of your own.

This book is designed to spread awareness and help the autistic community find a platform for change. Traditional approaches to autism need to be changed, and as a parent, it is my responsibility to do that. Autistic children, and to a lesser degree, ADHD children, experience the world in a different manner, and our focus needs to be on a difference, not a disability, abnormality, or special needs.

You may have heard the terms "neurotypical" and "neurodiverse," which I explain in detail. The idea is that autistic children have neurodiverse minds, with a focus on the diverse part. Neurotypical refers, for these purposes, to non-autistic individuals who experience life in a different manner than their neurodiverse counterparts. I set out the differences in terms of cognitive and brain function, in addition to the ways in which neurotypical people are different from each other.

I place focus on the type of language that should be used in the pursuit of affirming language that promotes inclusion as opposed to isolation. Words are powerful and have the ability to cause emotional distress. We do not want that.

Studies suggest that telling children that they are autistic at a younger age allows for a better quality of life as they grow older. (Cage, E. et al, 2017.). That aspect is explored from a results-based point of view and also from a human point of view. Interestingly, the identification of autistic boys is easier than the identification of autistic girls, which I explain in conjunction with the unique world experience that autistic individuals have.

I place focus on a woman by the name of Eustacia Cutler, who faced difficulties raising an autistic child in the 1950s. As one can imagine, the stigma in those days was huge, but Cutler refused to accept it and brought up her daughter in a household that promoted the celebration of difference. I also explain how Cutler's daughter, Dr. Temple Grandin, handled herself through life as an autistic person.

The sensory experience for autistic children is particularly difficult, and contrary to popular belief, we have eight senses. I laid out what those senses are and how they impact the quality of life of autistic children. One has to remember that dealing with sensory overload is a big challenge, and I pay attention to the different sensory-stimulating behaviors that contribute to coping mechanisms. Expanding on this concept, there is a section on management via self-regulatory behavior and how parents and educators can assist in the development of these behaviors in a positive manner. I then move on to address emotional and cognitive control as well as visual, auditory, and olfactory regulation. Sensory integration therapy is the next theme, with examples of exercises that parents and educators can implement.

Empathy can be a problematic skill for autistic individuals, and Dr. Damian Milton's "double empathy" theory, which I explore, details the hurdles in understanding the experiences of others in an empathetic way. Another point of focus on the social development of autistic children is Michelle Garcia Winner's company, Social Thinking ©. Garcia has been instrumental in explaining how we make sense of life through what is called our meaning maker, which provides us with context.

I discuss the social challenges that autistic children have, from adapting to varying social situations to understanding sarcasm, displaying manners, and engaging in back-and-forth conversation as well as initiating conversation. I explain how parents can prepare their autistic children for these situations via exercises that allow the identification of social cues. Communication forms a large part of this section, specifically communication in friendships. The four levels of friendship— acquaintance, casual, close, and intimate—are dealt with in a way that shows parents and educators how to give autistic children a more meaningful sense of relationships.

The next section handles sports and how autistic children can benefit from social interactions through sports. Furthermore, the preference is individual sports, but with others, such as horseback riding or martial arts.

The three "R's" of bullying are brought into focus, i.e., recognize, respond, and report, before a short section that re-emphasizes empathy.

Constructive language follows, along with the importance of describing things in a way that is conducive to inclusion. I do use "high-functioning" and "low-functioning," although that is not ideal. However, they form the basis of human application, not just autistic function. As part of this section, routines, specific interests, food preferences, social anxiety, and overwhelm are dealt with in detail, followed by an analysis of the three levels of autism and the corresponding levels of support each one requires.

The focus turns to highlighting information regarding different programs at schools that allow the integration of autistic children with neurotypicals. Specifically, IEPs, give parents the opportunity to work in conjunction with educators and therapists, to develop programs suitable to the support needs of their autistic children.

Sadly, autistic individuals do not have a long-life span, on average. The reason for self-harm is that depression and other mental health problems are known to accompany autism. I also note the difficulties with healthcare, including affordability, then bring attention to the appropriateness of the infinity symbolism of autism as opposed to the puzzle piece. This section concludes with explanations as to how autism is not just a neurotype, including some information on the nuts and bolts of "neuro" and what the ramifications of late identification of autism are.

I move forward to assess what emotions are evoked when your child is identified as autistic. It can be a tough time, and feelings of anger or regret about parenting techniques are common. On the other hand, relief is also felt quite regularly, and there is a grief cycle specific to what happens after finding out that your child is autistic. The cycle is explored and explained prior to acceptance.

Two pieces of writing, *Welcome to Holland*, and *Welcome to Beirut*, form part of my analysis. The former looks at what it is like to find out that your child has down syndrome and how it affects parenting thereafter. The latter is somewhat of a parody of the former but explains the same subject after receiving news that your child is autistic.

Parenting is stressful, as we all know, and as parents, we need to take time for ourselves. This particular section is about maintaining the correct mindset, taking life day by day with a bit of forward planning, but also being kind to yourself as a parent. I delve into mindfulness techniques, which promote presence and focus on the now. These techniques can be implemented by the parents and introduced to their children in efforts to improve the quality of life for both.

The last section looks at hope for the future, and the fact that autistic individuals have unique personalities, even though challenges are abundant. The "Big Five" personality model is explored, as well as the positive and negative manifestations thereof. Finally, I set out the theory of mind, and its categorization of deficit, before signing off with a challenge to prove the theory wrong, as your child grows into a person of value, through the ability to give and receive love.

Chapter 1:

How the Neurodivergent Mind

Works

Neurodiversity is a term that many people, even parents of autistic children, may not be aware of. As the name suggests, the concept is based on the premise that our minds are diverse to the point where we experience the world in vastly different ways. Our brains are so intricate that it is not possible for us all to see the world in the same way. There is no right way of experiencing life, meaning that thoughts and behaviors that would have previously been classified as "deficits" should be reclassified simply as differences.

Different Types of Neurodivergence

This book is specifically focused on neurodivergence in autism and Attention Deficit Hyperactivity Disorder (ADHD). However, I will list the other types of neurodiversity for the sake of completeness before directing focus to autism and ADHD:

- Tourette's Syndrome

- Dyslexia

- Dyspraxia

- Dyscalculia

- Dysgraphia

- Meares-Irlen Syndrome

- Hyperlexia

- Synaesthesia

- Aspergers

- Pathological Demand Avoidance

- Sensory Processing Disorder

Neurodivergence can also be said to encompass mental illnesses such as schizophrenia and bipolar disorder, but the jury is still out on the accuracy of this idea. Interestingly, neurodivergence goes beyond differences in function, depending on the type of neurodivergence at its core. Gender, race, and culture also play a significant role, which makes logical sense considering that those three categories experience life differently as it is.

What Makes Neurodivergent Brains Different?

The best way of addressing the differences in a neurodivergent brain is by drawing comparisons with a neurotypical brain. The former, as explained above, manifests in various **conditions,** but an all-encompassing conclusion is that neurodivergent brains experience difficulties with soft skills. This is a term that is often used in relation to employment but fundamentally applies to social interactions in general. An example is speaking too loudly or standing uncomfortably close to someone in public. In times of stress, neurodivergent individuals may rock back and forth as a self-soothing exercise, which is also a hallmark of struggles with soft skills.

Further differences include irregularity of mood and an unconscious reluctance to pay attention to stimuli. Neurodivergent individuals may vary in behavior, often when approaching learning or sociability. The idea that these manifestations are different, not abnormal, largely rejects the medical model of disability, which is discussed in further detail later in this book.

The neurotypical brain is commonly acknowledged as one that displays typical cognitive ability and intellectual application. Individuals falling into this category meet traditionally accepted developmental milestones within a relatively standardized time period. Other accepted characteristics of neurotypical behavior include the ability to recognize when one is standing too close to another or speaking too loudly, given the social setting. The observable presumption is that communication skills and developing social connections without being overcome by noise or light, for example, are relatively easy for neurotypical brains.

As parents, friends, employers, or colleagues of Autistic or ADHD children and young adults, it is important to understand that the terms neurodivergent and neurotypical go a long way toward encompassing differences and putting aside the idea of abnormality. The use of language is perhaps more important than one may think.

Affirming Language

Take a simple exercise that is done day in and day out by parents and educators around the world when teaching language to young children. A picture of a cat is shown to the child, with the word "cat" written below. With repetition, the child learns to associate what they see with the word that is used to describe it. The repetition part is the affirmation that the picture and the word are linked.

Parents who call their children stupid are affirming stupidity, even though that may not be the case. If someone hears something over and over again, they will start to believe it. For these reasons, it is necessary to change the way that we use language in the realm of autism and ADHD. Remember, differences are not deficiencies!

Emma Ward, artist, autism advocate, and mother of four, encapsulated the concept brilliantly, and I quote: "The way we talk to our children is how they will talk about themselves. I choose to surround my family with voices that raise us up" (Ward, E, n.d.).

As a start, let's look at autism, fully described as Autistic Spectrum Disorder. The term "disorder" is problematic. When we think of a disorder, the conclusion is that something is wrong or has gone wrong. However, relabeling autism in its full form as Autistic Spectrum Difference, removes the misapprehension that something is wrong and replaces it with the notion that something is different.

The same thinking applies to the following:

- Sensory Processing Difference, not Sensory Processing Disorder.

- My child is autistic, not my child has autism.

- Identified as autistic, not diagnosed with autism.

- Inclusive education, not special education.

- Passions or hobbies, not restricted interests, or obsessions.

These subtle differences in semantics can have a significant impact on how a child views themselves as a person. In a child's formative years, parental influence is what shapes the child, which is why parents need to use affirming language to validate and celebrate their autistic identity. The same must apply to educators. Teachers and therapists are next in line as influential figures in the young lives of children. Parents give up a lot of power and influence when they drop their kids off at school or at therapy, which is why educators need to practice inclusivity. It is likely that an autistic or ADHD child has heard words such as "disorder," "treatment," "symptoms," or "abnormal" from doctors and other medical people. This type of language affirms abnormality, and it is the job of educators and parents to dispel those words with inclusive affirmations centered around difference. Admittedly, medical professionals should also be using the correct affirmations. However, when parents with autistic or ADHD children start seeing doctors for the first time, they have no idea what harm the traditionally used language can cause.

The ramifications of using the "old language" can place limitations on autistic or ADHD children. Self-esteem issues, insecurities, an altered sense of identity, and acceptance of "being broken" can stay with a child into adulthood. The terms "high-functioning" and "low-functioning" are particularly damaging and can also be frustrating when heard by parents. On one hand, the use of the term's reeks of ignorance, and on the other, people use them innocently. No matter who you are, your functional abilities differ on a daily basis. Late nights make one tired and affect work performance, as well as general day-to-day activities. So why do we label differences in autistic and ADHD children in such a way as to affirm that there is something wrong? The correct terms are "specific strengths" and "needs," which terms apply to every human alive.

Autistic children need therapy, educational strategies, and love, not treatments or interventions. They do not have special needs; they do have individual needs. Autistic children are non-speaking, not nonverbal. They have an intricate language without the need to speak. Autistic children do not have anything wrong with them. They are different, as are we all, and as parents and educators, we need to affirm that.

Does Teaching a Child That They Are Autistic at a Younger Age Create Better Adult Outcomes?

Several studies have been conducted on this subject. The most relevant study is a very recent one, which I will summarize. The full citation is contained in the references section, as the study was conducted by several academics (Oredipe et al., 2022). No similar study has ever been done, and the only available research suggests that support given to autistic children in the past did lead to better adult outcomes. Past studies may have glossed over the concept of telling children at young ages that they are autistic, or perhaps such a concept was just not part of the study. Either way, the 2022 study indicates progress and is a very welcome one.

Seventy-eight university students participated and were asked three questions, as follows:

- How did you learn that you were autistic?

- How did you feel about autism when you first learned that you were autistic?

- When would you tell autistic children about their autism?

The fundamental findings were:

- A higher quality of life and well-being as adults were present in the students who were told that they were autistic when they were young children.

- Learning at an older age that one is autistic showed associations with more positive emotions and also a higher quality of life.

The above two conclusions may be easily conflated, but the major difference is quality of life as opposed to feelings about one's autism. However, the common denominator was being told at a young age.

The follow-on findings were:

- The students who were told that they were autistic in later life did display positive emotions towards autism.

- A possible reason is the sense of relief that was felt in discovering that there was an explanation for their differences.

- The study suggested that the students who learned that they were autistic later in life may be better placed to interact with autistic communities and become involved in the neurodivergent movement.

Shared experiences are a tool that brings people together, and it was found that some children and young teenagers first felt negative emotions after being told that they were autistic. Positivity grew with age and the discovery of other autistic individuals with whom they could talk about past experiences.

Not one of the students said that they would wait until adulthood. In fact, some were of the opinion that they would tell their children as soon as they became old enough to understand. One particular student articulated the way that they would tell their child very well, and to quote directly: "I would tell my child that autism is a different way of thinking, that it can be challenging and beautiful and powerful and exhausting and impactful, that autistic people deserve to be themselves, to be proud of their identity, and to have supports that help them meet their needs."

The study clearly shows that a child who learns they are autistic at a younger age is better prepared for greater well-being and quality of life. Furthermore, being told at a younger age allows for learning from life experiences, making it easier to attain said well-being and quality of life. The resounding outcome is that it is most definitely the case that teaching a child that they are autistic at a younger age creates better adult outcomes.

How Do Gender Differences Impact Children With Neurodivergent Minds?

Research shows that autistic boys and girls may experience autism in different ways. Girls tend to be identified as autistic later than boys, but interestingly, autistic boys outnumber girls significantly. This has been attributed to the biological differences between the sexes. However, the manner in which neurodivergence manifests in autistic boys and girls may explain the different impact on young neurodivergent minds.

According to research, for every autistic girl, there are four autistic boys (de Giambattista et al., 2021). Signs or traits of autism differ only slightly between boys and girls and can therefore be easily missed, leading to a misinterpretation of support needs in girls. It has been suggested that one of the reasons is that girls tend to camouflage or mask. These terms are addressed in Chapter 3, but in summary, they refer to hiding differences, which they perceive to indicate an abnormality.

Unique Interpretation of the World

We have all experienced some form of social anxiety, be it discomfort in large crowds or even being nervous about a job interview. With autistic children, social and other anxieties are amplified, which means that they see and experience the world uniquely. It can be a confusing experience, often characterized by sensory overload. It is as if too much information is whirling around in the brain, leading to displays of differences such as tantrums and social withdrawal. I must reiterate that such displays are merely different coping mechanisms.

In a visual sense, autistic children, in some cases, have a higher awareness of peripheral vision. As one can imagine, this creates a situation where the perception of the environment is more intense. It is almost as if too much is happening at once, which leads to an uncomfortable placement, a looping-over effect, and confusion as to the experience of time and space.

The Stigma

Autism is not a mental illness, although autistic individuals do have a propensity for mental illness. This means that autism is subject to a double stigma: The mental health stigma and the incorrect perception that autism is a disease or sickness. It can be infuriating to consider that people think that depression is a case of "just cheer up" or that autism is a "problem on the fringe of society." For these reasons, more education is required on these topics to dispel ignorance and empower those who are subject to the stigma.

To really address the stigma described above, it is useful to define what a stigma is. The Encyclopedia Britannica's definition is as follows:

"A set of negative and often unfair beliefs that a society or group of people have about something."

Every stigma is slightly different, but there are shared elements. The autism stigma could be said to be unique in that it garners rejection, which is not necessarily the case with stigmas about being poor, homosexual, or mentally ill, for example. Individuals may be weary, frightened, or uncomfortable when they observe different reactions to sensory stimuli by autistic children or adults, for that matter. An ill-timed laugh, a panic attack, or a tantrum might violate the "rules of society," for lack of a better term, and non-autistic people could very well become judgmental.

I don't like the term "violation," as it leans towards the negative. However, it is the correct description in this case. What I mean is the violation of personal space. Autism is synonymous with a lack of spatial awareness, and violating someone else's space is a common occurrence. If an autistic child is standing at a distance considered too close to another child or adult, the other person may not even realize that the child is autistic. The discomfort of the individual may lead to irritation and lashing out, which could cause a reaction that reveals the child's autism and casts judgment upon that child. The reaction feeds the child's thoughts of rejection and perpetuates the "there is something wrong with me" mindset in the child.

One may argue that children lack the cognition to understand the damage that they can do to other children through exclusion and bullying. Unfortunately, autistic children are often not included in activities with peers and are subjected to being picked on. This is not necessarily stigma-related, as it can be further argued that children are excluded based on overt differences, like being overweight. Perhaps one could call it an unconscious propagation of the stigma.

Parents and siblings of autistic or ADHD children are also affected by the stigma. Parenting requires social interactions at events like school plays or children's birthday parties, which are occasions that could trigger anxiety in autistic children, causing socially frowned-upon actions.

Parents of other children might avoid parents with autistic children, stop inviting them to gatherings, and avoid them at extracurricular activities. The difficulty is that children ask questions. It is difficult to explain to a child the reasons for not being accepted into social environments anymore. Parents can also feel judged and labeled as bad parents, which is just not fair.

How Exactly Do We Break the Stigma?

To break the stigma, we need to raise awareness and get people talking about autism and ADHD. These things tend to happen slowly, but we have to start somewhere. Social media allows an unprecedented reach that can help to inform and educate. Perhaps high schools can adopt programs that explain autism and affirm that behavior is different, not wrong, or abnormal. There is a day dedicated to autism awareness (April 2), but we need more than that.

Mainstream media is a means that has been used to spread knowledge and understanding on many taboo subjects, as well as dispel stigmas and misapprehensions that people have. There is a Netflix series called *Atypical,* which I strongly recommend as an educational tool for autism. The main protagonist is an eighteen-year-old autistic boy who is negotiating his way through his teenage life. His behaviors and depiction of what autism is like are very accurate. The show addresses the way in which the world is viewed by the character and the challenges he faces. It also focuses on his family support system and points out the prejudices that are present in real life. The series, which debuted in August 2017, is perhaps a starting point for people interested in learning more about autism and understanding the stigma. If one can understand the stigma, one can start to break it.

Eustacia Cutler and the Autism Stigma

Eustacia Cutler is known worldwide amongst the autism community and has done groundbreaking work on spreading information about autism. Cutler is a former singer and actor, now a speaker and author, and the mother of an autistic daughter. Dr. Temple Grandin. Cutler's association with autism began back in 1950, when her daughter was identified as autistic. During that time in history, there were tremendously powerful stigmas attached to homosexuality, feminism, and racial oppression, so autism stood no chance.

In 1950, autism was seen as a "developmental disability," and many autistic children were institutionalized in stark, gray-stone buildings with poor care, left to feel isolated and alone. Cutler would not have it, and despite her husband's being in favor of putting their daughter in an institution, Cutler refused and decided that Temple would be raised at home.

Cutler struggled to find schools that would accept Temple and heard things such as, "She is a menace to society," "She is retarded," and "She does not belong at a 'normal'" school (Laird, n.d.). New therapies were hard to come by, and Cutler had scant support from her then-husband, but she persisted with what she felt was the best way to raise an autistic child. With age, Temple excelled in academia, and as of 2022, she is an animal behaviorist at Colorado State University. Temple is an advocate for the humane treatment of animals and a beacon of light for autistic children. We all need role models, and teaching children about people such as Cutler and her very successful autistic daughter is a way of providing role models in autism.

I came across an online article by a woman named Chloe Fay, which I have referenced at the end of this book. Fay has a BA in Special

Education, and while I do not like the term "special," the nine points listed are very applicable to changing the way we see autism.

Furthermore, the article is very helpful in giving parents and educators a push in the right direction toward breaking the stigma:

- Learn about the history of autism.

- Raise awareness with what you wear.

- Check out the work of famous people with autism.

- Find sensory toys and tools that help.

- Support autism-friendly businesses and employees.

- Read books about autism.

- Spread awareness in your community.

- Spread kindness.

- Read, watch, or listen to something created by an autistic person.

Inge-Marie Eigsti, an autism expert and Ph.D. holder from the University of Rochester, is particularly interested in studies probing the effects of the stigma on families. Speaking about how autistic people look and speak like everyone else and the difficulty in understanding or accepting autistic individuals, Eigsti put forward this opinion (2016):

"For many families, that makes the presence of out-of-control behavior or socially unexpected behavior that much more stigmatizing because there is not a clear indicator of why the child is behaving like that. Parents may worry that the behavior is being attributed to bad parenting skills, laziness, a lack of motivation, or other negative qualities in the child or the family."

It is this type of thinking that needs to be dispelled by raising awareness. As I mentioned previously, a stigma is a set of NEGATIVE and UNFAIR beliefs. Autistic individuals must be treated in a positive and fair manner.

Chapter 2:

The Eight Senses

Eight Not Five

Most of us have learned that there are five senses: smell, sound, taste, touch, and sight. In reality, there are three more senses: vestibular, interoceptive, and proprioceptive. As we know, autism is synonymous with sensory overload, and dealing with eight enhanced senses provides its challenges. Let's have a look at those senses and some biological explanations.

Smell

The olfactory system in the brain is what controls the processing of smell. Situated in the forward part of the brain, the olfactory bulb is a conduit that links the brain to the nose.

The bulb operates by

- discriminating among odors.

- enhancing the detection of odors.

- filtering out background odors.

- allow modification in the detection of odors.

Autistic children may experience certain smells in an enhanced manner. The result can be an unwillingness to go to a place associated with a particular smell. A gas station is a good example; fuel has a distinctive smell, and autistic individuals could find that smell intense–an assault on the senses, if you like. Even ordinarily pleasant smells, like perfume or scented shampoo, can be overwhelming.

The resultant anxiety can be partially combated by not taking your autistic child anywhere where there is a likelihood of adverse odors.

Cleaning products can be particularly overwhelming for kids with smell sensitivity.

When at home, use unscented shampoo and keep the house well-ventilated.

On the other side of the scale, smells like deodorants or perfumes may be pleasant to autistic children, resulting in their seeking out those smells. Unusual social behavior may be a result, in terms of seeking out smells on people in public and moving too close to such people in order to take in the odors.

Enjoyable smells can be emulated by wearing strong perfume or carrying a scented handkerchief when in public. You could cook strongly scented meals at home, have nice-smelling flowers in the house, or even burn incense.

Always remember that your autistic child experiences differences, not abnormalities, so you need to continuously affirm that with positive language.

Sound

The auditory cortex, primarily located in the brain's left hemisphere, is tasked with processing sound. The system identifies changes in amplitude and frequency as well as computing combinations of frequencies. Research has shown that gifted musicians tend to have a more powerful auditory system, allowing them to pick up intricacies in sound differentiation that others might not be able to.

Studies suggest that autistic children who experience sound at amplified levels find that forty decibels are extremely loud. A conversation at close quarters is about fifty decibels, and a whispered conversation is around thirty decibels. Considering those statistics, then placing an autistic child in an environment such as a classroom, where conversations, shuffling papers, coughing, and the voice of the teacher are bombarding that child's ears, a severe amount of anxiety is inevitable.

Some therapists discourage the use of noise-canceling headphones. However, they really are a great tool for maintaining calm. Allowing allocated quiet time at home has also proved effective, as have distractions such as playing a game on a phone or iPad. It is all about making an environment as comfortable and non-distracting as possible as a tool to manage anxiety.

Taste

Taste is experienced via the gustatory system. The most commonly used example is the detection of salt. In a primal sense, humans require water, and salt makes us thirsty. The gustatory cortex tells us to add salt to our french fries, which enhances the taste but also creates the need to drink water. Communication is between the brain and the tongue, meaning that we have the ability to understand that biting into a lemon is sour and unpleasant while biting into a bar of chocolate is sweet and pleasurable.

Sensitivity to taste is complicated to solve, but taking your child to a nutritionist can help. You need to figure out which foods provide a horrible eating experience and which foods are nice to eat. It is not uncommon for autistic children to only enjoy a few food types. There is nothing wrong with that, and the way to cater to taste differences is to cook what your child likes and make sure he or she always has a packed snack when not at home. It is not ideal, but it is not the worst thing in the world. Perhaps try to get some of the healthy foods into the pancake batter and mix them thoroughly, in which case your child may not notice. Having said that, malnutrition or vitamin and mineral deficits can creep in, which is another reason talking to a nutritionist might be a good idea.

Food textures, not taste, are often the problem. Many children prefer crunchy foods over soft and mushy foods. Neurodivergent children are aware when subtle changes are made to their food, which is why "hiding" the healthy foods in soups and batters can sometimes backfire. This, in turn, could potentially cause a child to reject foods they previously consumed. If they have a limited food repertoire to begin with, this can easily turn problematic.

Touch

Identification through touch is regulated by the somatosensory cortex. It is a complex system that also controls the sensations of pressure, temperature, and pain. These sensory feelings are not all strictly touch-related, but the diversity of brain function in this specific area encapsulates them as the primary components of touch.

The term "touchy-feely" comes to mind. Some people prefer a hug, others a handshake or a high five. Autistic children sometimes prefer no form of touch at all. Managing that at home can be very challenging, although emotions regarding a lack of affection may arise in parents or siblings. We still need to encourage acceptance of the differences, even though it is extremely tough. Fear of light touch is incredibly difficult to manage because touch is unavoidable. However, educators and parents can slowly introduce touch for brief periods in order to create acclimatization to touch, leading to less anxiety (Cekaite, 2016). Remember to use a firm touch instead of a light touch. A light touch is arousing to the sympathetic nervous system and can cause a fight-or-flight reaction. Firm touch can inhibit or dampen down the arousal that light touch causes and make touch more tolerable.

Sight

Sight manifests as visual pathways, i.e., neuroscientists distinguish between two visual systems. The "what" system is located at the junction of the occipital lobe and the temporal lobe and is involved in object recognition. The "where" system is located on the junction of the occipital and parietal lobes and is involved in location information (Goldberg, 2022).

The occipital lobe has connections with the parietal and temporal lobes, and this is how visual information is interpreted, resulting in the development of visual perceptual skills. Many autistic individuals have significant strengths in visual perception skills. They will gravitate, at an early age, toward the letters of the alphabet, colors, numbers, geometric shapes, and other types of puzzles.

Visual stimulatory behavior will often involve holding an object very close to one's face, then moving it quickly past one's face. Autistic children are often also fascinated by a rolling or spinning object. Autistic children are often sensitive to the flickering light (as well as to the buzzing sound) of fluorescent lighting. Fabric filters can be hung under fluorescent ceiling lights to dim the effect, or incandescent lighting can be used instead.

Autistic children can be extremely sensitive to light and very specific about colors. Dimmer switches are a good tool to regulate light at home, and sunglasses help in outdoor settings. Preference to one color can be changed by slowly introducing different colored toys or clothing, not that there is anything wrong with a propensity to only one or two colors.

Proprioception

Internal body mapping results from the nervous system's proprioceptive input when infants engage in random movements of their arms and legs. This forms the basis for all motor planning skills, from something as simple as reaching for a ball to something as complex as learning to tie your shoes as a five-year-old. Often, kids with ASD have poor proprioceptive processing, which results in poor motor planning skills, which may result in difficulty with gross or fine motor skills, including oral motor speech and sound production.

Proprioceptive input can regulate and calm the nervous system. I had a student many years ago who was around age three. We often found him laying between the mattress and the box spring of his bed because he liked the feeling of the weight on his body. He instinctively provided himself with proprioceptive input (needed to regulate his nervous system). Today, you can buy a weighted blanket at a store or order a weighted vest online.

Graded muscle control is a function of proprioceptive input. How do you know how hard to push on your pencil without breaking the tip? Those with poor proprioceptive processing will likely use excessive force and fail to understand how to grade their movement. How can you pick up a Styrofoam cup without crushing it if you have poor muscle control? You can't.

There are various fun activities that can be done at home to teach your child how to use physical prowess in order to reduce the intensity of interactions. An obstacle course using different items and requiring lifting, jumping, and turning is a very useful tool. Throwing a ball back and forth, then moving further away, can assist in creating awareness of the speed with which the ball is thrown in relation to distance. You can give your child body massages using varying levels of pressure to illustrate what is too hard and what is too soft. Look at it like preparation for an athletic event by honing the skills needed to participate at intensity levels that are measured and appropriate in social situations.

Vestibular

Balance and motion activation are controlled by the vestibular system, found in the middle ear. Spatial awareness is also controlled by the vestibular system and is something that autistic children struggle to discern. Sports and outdoor activities can help in developing better balance, which also has a positive effect on spatial awareness. Skateboarding, gymnastics, or even skipping will improve balance and give a better understanding of motion. Musical chairs work, as well as dancing, so be creative and cater to your child's different requirements.

Interoception

Interoception is the manner in which communication with internal organs manifests. Autistic children can face situations where feelings of hunger, thirst, warmth, or cold cannot be identified. Teaching children about their bodies by using charts or explaining the cues from our bodies—telling us that we are hungry, tired, or cold—can go a long way toward creating specific awareness. Being unable to identify these body cues can certainly be changed by asking your child whether he or she is hungry or thirsty. Slowly, they will learn that after an exercise, it is likely that they are hungry or that going outside in the winter will make them cold.

Sensory Diet

Taking note of how autistic children process sensory information and then adapt to their environments, as discussed above, can be called "sensory management." It certainly isn't an easy task, but seeing your child's quality of life improves as you implement activities and take measures to cater to their specific needs will be rewarding beyond comprehension. It is typically the role of the Occupational Therapist to assess how an individual processes sensory input and to subsequently develop a "sensory diet" or a specific program of sensory activities that help improve sensory processing and self-regulation.

Self-Regulation

We should all work at self-regulation, and as the name suggests, the practice is one of management in day-to-day life. It requires personal awareness and greater control over how we conduct ourselves. Dr. Temple Grandin, who was mentioned in the previous chapter, offers her own definition as follows:

"The skill of managing feelings so that they don't reach overwhelming levels and interfere with learning and development. Many people on the spectrum need support as they struggle to manage their emotions and mitigate their anxiety."

Even as adults, perhaps especially as adults, we experience emotions that are difficult to regulate. Oversensitivity, anger, impatience, or anxiety can prove problematic. Learning self-regulation from a young age is a step in the right direction for developing skills that can be carried into adulthood. It is widely accepted that self-regulation can be broken up into three categories.

Sensory Regulation

Gives autistic children the skills to identify potentially anxiety-inducing sensory experiences and to respond in a way that mitigates the potential anxiety.

Emotional Regulation

As an aside, it is a pity that social conventions impose rules upon us, restricting the things that we would like to say. We experience a semi-forced suppression of opinions because of politeness, and in autistic children, teaching "socially acceptable" moderation of reactions is the name of the game.

Cognitive Regulation

This involves the shaping of thinking processes for the purposes of greater focus on learning, problem-solving, and persistence.

Implementation

The Zones of Regulation (Kuypers, L.) is a book that sets out a curriculum developed by Leah Kuypers, MA Ed. The curriculum has been adopted by educators and parents around the world and is considered the foremost approach to self-regulation in autistic children. Kuypers is an expert in the field of autism and has worked as an occupational therapist at various public schools in the United States.

Helping Your Children With Self-Regulation

As you may remember, in chapter one, I referred to studies about children benefiting from being told at a young age that they are autistic. One of the students in the study described autism as "challenging and beautiful, powerful, exhausting, and impactful." Such is the journey that educators, and more importantly, parents, walk with autistic children; self-regulation is an important part of that journey.

Stimulatory Behavior

Stimulatory behavior, known as "stimming" or "self-stimming," is often observed in individuals with autism. The practices of rocking back and forth, walking up and down, tapping a pen incessantly, or flicking an elastic band are examples of stimulating behavior that acts as a comfort in overwhelming or anxiety-inducing situations. There is nothing wrong with stimming, and we often do it without even noticing, but it can become disruptive and get in the way of learning. A balance needs to be reached, and the idea is to reduce, change, or introduce replacement stimming exercises that may cause an autistic child to be singled out and isolated. It is simple and complicated at the same time. Let's take the pen-tapping example in a classroom. A good replacement behavior is a foot-tapping at a measured rhythm while reciting "one, two, three, four." If a child can engage in the latter and still draw out the comfort required, then the distraction is almost entirely removed. Parents need to practice with their autistic children at home and slowly introduce behavior notifications or changes.

Any routine is difficult to break or alter, which is why constant work is required, especially considering that stimming will always be present in some form. To use another example, autistic children may struggle to contain the excitement, so jumping up and down, with hand clapping and shrieks, is not unusual. The unfortunate part is that in public places, people stare, and that can negatively affect the child and the child's family. In this instance, the idea is to regulate the behavior so as to create a culture of a shorter, less intense display of excitement. Working on regulating self-stimulatory behavior has shown to have positive effects on the alienation that autistic children can feel as a result of unwanted negative attention during periods of self-stimulatory behavior.

I want to add something about the fact that because we do not want to encourage the masking of self-stimulatory behavior, we need to consider some things, including our individual perspectives on the issue.

Educators of all kinds should be teaching their neurotypical students about why their autistic peers need to self-stimulate. It's to regulate their nervous systems. Yes, it's a difficult concept to understand, but if it is phrased correctly, it can make sense to even the youngest student.

Schools in every state should acknowledge the need for Occupational Therapy services that will address ways to help kids regulate their nervous systems, so the need to self-stim is reduced in the classroom. Sensory integration services are most certainly educationally relevant.

Visual, Auditory, and Olfactory Stimming

Visual

Like other stimming activities, repetition is often a convention of visual stimming. Flicking a light switch on and off, following moving objects with one's eyes, or staring at the television are regular occurrences. Sensory lighting is a good way of creating self-regulation and reducing stress.

Auditory

Again, repetition is evident in auditory stimming and may involve playing a song over and over or making indistinguishable noises for extended periods. An effective method of self-regulation in these instances is maybe something like a bubble tube, which is literally a tube that makes gentle, enjoyable, calming bubbling sounds.

Olfactory

Biting, sniffing, and touching characterize olfactory stimulation and can result in unpleasant experiences when trying food and drinks that are either very bitter or very sweet. To prevent unpleasant experiences, it is necessary to teach children what is beneficial and what is harmful, so the child is aware of what to smell, eat, or touch. Remember, one of the functions of the senses is to protect us from danger, so if the milk smells sour, most neurotypicals know to avoid it. However, in some instances, this may be more of a scenario where one must learn from the unpleasant experience.

The Sensory Funnel

The sensory funnel, created by Aspergers Experts Co-Founder Danny Raede, is divided into five groups that sit on top of each other, reflected in a hypothetical funnel shape. We address the groups from bottom to top—sensory first, followed by emotion, awareness, social skills, and finally, executive function. Raede's Sensory Funnel was developed as a visual tool to showcase the importance of the order in which we must address the needs of neurodivergent. Raede's theory certainly makes sense. How can you really focus, learn, or understand how to improve your social skills or executive function abilities when you are experiencing the discomfort of your body or brain feeling dysregulated?

Sensory

The eight senses, but more specifically, the feelings precipitated by your body, such as anxiety, can perpetuate through throat constriction, increased heart rate, and nervous energy.

Emotional

This category sits above sensory and is the result of anxiety. One can look at it as the sensory experience triggering an emotional reaction.

Awareness

Emotional overload limits awareness, and the focus is purely on the emotional experience, which limits the ability to take in anything else.

Social

Social skills and reading situations can be difficult for autistic children. However, this is something that can be learned through observation, teaching, and practice. To be more specific, autistic children may not understand nonverbal language, such as body language, or they may struggle with how to interpret things said in a conversation.

Executive Function

This can be looked at as the final goal and can be summed up as the ability to be highly functional in environments that have traditionally been anxiety- or stress-inducing.

The following points provide the definition of the term:

- Adaptable thinking: Adjusting to the situation when need be.

- Planning: Thinking about the future, prioritizing, and creating a plan.

- Self-Monitoring: Evaluate how you are doing.

- Self-Control: Maintaining composure despite feelings and emotions.

- Time management: Planning and organizing a schedule to complete a large assignment or time-consuming task.

- Organization: Arranging things in order to maintain some sort of system.

Sensory Integration

Our brains interpret the way in which we react to experiencing feelings and emotions based on our eight senses in different situations. Integration comes in as the function that joins the processing of a combination of different senses. The good news is that scientific analysis has shown that therapeutic assistance has enjoyed success in regulating the unpleasant processing of sensory interpretation. Sensory integration is primarily the interconnection between tactile, proprioceptive, and vestibular functions.

Sensory Integration Therapy (SIT)

SIT is by no means new; it was first explored in the 1970s by an occupational therapist and psychologist A. Jean Ayres. SIT is a therapeutic approach that is used by Occupational Therapists to improve symptoms of sensory integration dysfunction.

One should involve the therapist in guiding the child through the "just right" challenge of navigating sensory activities in order to improve sensory processing and produce an "adaptive response" on the part of the child. Ayres theorized that the behavior and learning problems were, in part, due to faulty integrations of sensory information and the inability of higher centers to modulate and regulate lower brain sensory-motor centers (Ayers, 1972).

Sensory Processing

This was partially dealt with in the prior examination of the eight senses, but for the sake of completeness: The perception of the senses, followed by the manner in which the senses are understood, and the arrangement of the sensory experience make up what is called "sensory processing."

What Is the Difference Between Sensory Integration and Sensory Processing?

The terms are used interchangeably, and it may be argued that the differences are subtle, if not absent. The bottom line is that both terms refer to the brain receiving information and instructing the body to act in accordance with that information.

Sensory Modulation Difficulties

It can be challenging to gauge the intensity required in reactions to sensory input, which often gives the impression of a misbehaving child or a bad parent. Being over-responsive to sensory input is just as normal as being under-responsive. The latter conjures ideas that a child is disinterested, absorbed in themselves, and unwilling to participate, in a classroom setting, for instance. Over-responsiveness is on the other side of the scale and involves extreme excitement, which is characterized by shouting, making noises, fidgeting, and unfortunately, being disruptive during class. It can be exceptionally difficult to tailor or modulate different behaviors, but if successful, it can create a much better quality of life.

Remember, a tantrum from a neurotypical child is completely different from a perceived tantrum from an autistic child. In fact, autistic children are experiencing sensory overload, which looks like a tantrum to an outsider but is not an *actual* tantrum. Scientifically, the amygdala is triggered. This is the fight-or-flight response area of the brain, which takes effect upon sensory overload.

Sensory Discrimination and Perceptual Problems

Discrimination is the brain's ability to interpret information and disregard its irrelevant parts. In autistic children, the brain can mix up information or organize it in a way that does not correspond with the sensory stimuli. There are a whole host of instances in which this occurs, but below is a list of the more frequently observed manifestations of difficulty with sensory discrimination, as in the inability to:

- Describe or identify objects through touch and/or sight.

- Discern taste differences.

- Judge how loudly or softly to speak.

- Pay attention to others.

- Perceive depth, elevation, or distance.

- Judge how much force to use when picking up an object, throwing a ball, or closing a door.

- Recognize hunger or thirst.

- Identify that they need to use the bathroom.

Vestibular Bilateral Functioning Problems

Autistic children who experience vestibular-bilateral functioning problems lack awareness of their bodies and the space that they are in. The manifestations can be difficulties in maintaining good posture and a neutral head position using the two sides of the body together, as well as disorientation, stumbling, and general clumsiness.

Sympathetic Nervous System

We have all heard of "fight-or-flight," and this categorization is responsible for our defense mechanism when faced with a situation that is terrifying or fear-inducing. Another name is the Mobilization System or the Aggressive Defense System. On one end are anger and rage, while on the other end are fear and panic. When a distress signal is sent from the part of the brain called the amygdala, the hypothalamus activates the sympathetic nervous system by sending signals through the autonomic nerves to the adrenal glands. Epinephrine (adrenaline) and norepinephrine (noradrenaline) are released, which cause an accelerated heart rate, widening of the bronchial passages, and decreased motility (movement) of the large intestine.

Constricted blood vessels cause pupil dilation, activate goose bumps, induce sweating, and raise blood pressure. Some neurodivergent children and adults have an overactive Sympathetic Nervous System because they are stressed by what appears to neurotypicals as everyday things. Remember, what looks, feels, and smells perfectly fine to a neurotypical might feel tortuous to a neurodivergent, resulting in the neurodivergent's body setting off the fight-or-flight response right there at the breakfast table when trying to gobble down the soggy cereal. We would expect it to go off when we are fighting off a life threat or to flee from an enemy.

How sad and uncomfortable for our kiddos to be experiencing this rapid heartbeat and sweating while trying to choke down their cereal.

Sensory Seeking vs. Sensory Avoiding

The concept is simple: Some autistic children enjoy certain sensory experiences and seek them out. Others find similar sensory experiences awful and seek to avoid them. Here are a few examples:

Seeking

- Enjoy different smells
- Prefer being barefoot
- Give bear hugs frequently
- Love being tickled
- Making excessively loud noises

Avoiding

- Does not like being touched
- Finds loud noises unpleasant
- Removes labels from clothes due to the feel on the skin
- Very picky with food
- Turns lights off

Sensory Input

The American Psychological Association (ASA) Dictionary of Psychology defines *sensory input* as "the stimulation of a sense organ, causing a nerve impulse to travel to its appropriate destination in the brain or spinal cord." To break that down, the response given by a sensory organ when it is stimulated is the actual input. The sensory organs are, of course, the eyes, tongue, skin, ears, and nose.

Sensory Seeking Expanded

Further to the bullet points above, sensory seeking does require more detail, specifically in terms of activities that can create better organizational interactions with the world in general. Deep pressure is encouraged, using a foam roller to activate muscle movement, for instance. Encourage your child to play outside, especially with activities such as climbing trees or riding a bicycle. Use a yoga ball as a seat during homework time, so your child can maintain movement in a positive way. Have pillow fights, play tag, or put music on and dance with your child. Remember that you know your child best, so be creative and tailor activities to his or her needs.

Sensory Avoiding Expanded

The differences between sensory seeking and avoiding are huge, as are the exercises that can help autistic children come to terms with and accept sensory experiences. As awful as it sounds, parents have to test out reactions to stimuli. If your autistic child does not like the feel of clothes, then offer options and note the reactions. Prepare your child for stress-inducing activities to allow mental preparation or anticipation. Cook meals that your child enjoys; get them to help you with the dishes so they can experience soapy water. In contrast to sensory seeking, there is a lot of trial and error, with much more talking and explaining.

Three Pivot Practice Stories

The Sensory Funnel

While meeting with one of my adult autistic students, we began discussing the sensory funnel. He clearly understood my brief explanation and stated it in this manner:

If I go to a venue or even if I am expected to go to a venue where everything is not going to work for me, I become anxious. For example, it depends on "Who" will be there, "Where" it will occur, "What" the activity will be, and "What" the food will be. If any one of those things is a sensory trigger, I won't want to go! On the other hand, if I am in a one-on-one situation with someone I know and in a familiar venue, I will be happy and calm. Don't try to teach me social skills when I am in an overloaded state!

Sensory Regulation to Avoid Others

One of my students was very gifted and able to attend a school for the arts. He could be picked out of a crowd easily as, in the middle of summer, he would be seen wearing a long-sleeved shirt, a tie, a woolen sport coat, and long pants. I was always curious about this and assumed that he wore it to calm his nervous system. As I got to know him better, I inquired about his garb. He admitted that he dressed this way to keep others from approaching him! And he reported that it was quite effective.

Unique Perspective

Many years ago, while working with a four-year-old child with autism, I attempted to get him to engage with me by both looking and listening. This little guy, while looking away, reported that "it hurts" to do both at the same time and said, "When I try to do both, I can't understand what you are saying!" I thanked him for clearly stating why he refused to engage visually. His sensory systems simply could not work together. The child was the teacher!

Chapter 3:

To Mask or Not to Mask

As mentioned earlier, girls seem to be better at masking than young boys. Masking, which is also called camouflaging, is the practice of acting in a way that would be seen as "normal" or "socially acceptable." It is not unique to autism, and if we think about it logically, we all engage in masking on an everyday basis. For example, you have an argument with your partner one morning before leaving for work. On the way, you stop for a coffee, and the server asks you how you are. You smile and tell that person that you are doing well when, in fact, you are upset and irritated by your partner. One could call that a mild form of masking because if every person in that situation answered the polite question, "How are you today?" in the actual way that they felt, nothing would ever get done.

Autistic children can be seen by the world as strange or different, which creates alienation. To avoid feelings of alienation, autistic children will act the way that their non-autistic peers act. Autistic children can suffer from social burnout or exhaustion from continued masking. The reason is that it takes a fair amount of thought and effort to remember to use the correct hand gestures, facial expressions, reactions, and discussions. The end goal for an autistic child who uses masking is to appear as if they are not different. Being different and experiencing the world differently is okay, normal, and should be socially acceptable. Although masking has been created as a social construct, there should not be a need for it, but it does occur. There are different types of masking, as well as different reasons for engaging in masking.

Types of masking:

- Disguising self-stimulating behavior
- Pre-scripting conversations
- Forcing eye contact
- Giving generic responses to questions
- Hiding personal interests
- Hiding anxiety or stress caused by sensory stimuli

Possible reasons for masking:

- Avoid bullying
- Make friends
- Avoiding the (unnecessary) stigma
- Fitting in
- Doing well in school

As one can imagine, having constant awareness and focusing on **not** being yourself most of the time is exhausting. A 2019 study published in the Journal of Autism and Developmental Disorders (Cage, E. et al, 2017) concluded that masking certainly has an adverse effect on mental health in autistic individuals. Stress and anxiety levels among participants in the survey were particularly high. Such is completely understandable, given that it is almost impossible to relax while knowing you have to mask the way you really are. Interestingly, it was found that interactions between autistic children and their parents at home showed a release of stress and anxiety. Often, the home environment is one in which autistic children take a reprieve from masking, which brings on the release of built-up stress and anxiety. Exhaustion also sits in this category, and one can imagine closing the front door after a long day of masking, breathing a huge sigh of relief, and collapsing onto one's bed, completely exhausted.

In 2017, Eilidh Cage, also part of the aforementioned 2019 study, along with two fellow researchers, interviewed 111 autistic adults in 2017 and concluded that those who actively engaged in masking had a much higher propensity for depression. Reverting back to childhood, it was proposed that telling children that they are autistic at a younger age is a good tool to alleviate masking, which in turn has positive ramifications for future mental health issues. (Cage, E. et al, V, 2017.).

In terms of suicidal thinking, masking on a continuous basis creates the self-imposed impression that the child is not good enough or is too different from everyone else. An autistic child who grows up believing that difference is a bad thing will focus on their differences in a negative manner. The commonly noted type of suicidal thinking can be described as a spoken sentence: "If I am dead, then I will not have any consciousness, which means that I will not have to hide my true self, which means that my stress, anxiety, depression, and pain will not exist anymore."

Autistic Burnout

Autistic burnout can manifest in several ways, including through neglect in looking after oneself. As parents of autistic children, it is important to ensure that your child is eating well and taking proper care of themselves. Going into adulthood and being unsupervised in times of burnout can result in poor eating, not washing or brushing teeth, not tidying up, and a loss of interest in doing any form of physical activity. Identifying burnout in your child and explaining what it is can go a long way toward reducing its severity as your child gets older and approaches adulthood. Difficulty regulating emotions is also a sign of burnout and is characterized by irritability, lack of patience, an unwillingness to communicate, and withdrawal from familiar activities. At the risk of over-stressing the point, we need to understand and educate autistic children on the results of masking, such as burnout, which predicts a better ability to manage emotions.

Loss of Identity

If a child gets so used to masking in order to create a life consistent with being accepted and included, he or she may start to become the mask and stray away from being the child. This is quite an often-observed phenomenon, not only in autistic children, but it can be excruciatingly difficult to have a sense of not knowing who you are anymore. There are arguments that masking is not necessarily a terrible behavior, but in situations where a child drifts through their younger years feeling lost and disenfranchised, it most certainly is.

Delayed Identification of autism

Simply put, masking is hiding. If a child begins masking from a young age, which is often the case, then parents and educators may have no way of identifying that a child is autistic. As mentioned above, girls tend to favor masking and be better at it than boys, which is why identifying an autistic girl child is more difficult than identifying an autistic boy child. Another difficulty is that, after identifying your child as autistic, the social belief that your child was not autistic but is now suddenly autistic can be harmful to children and parents. One can draw a comparison to depression outside of autism. The stigma makes many depressed individuals hide their depression in social interactions. If the time comes to open up about being depressed, friends and family who have observed the fake-happy persona may label the depressive as a "drama queen" or an "attention seeker." The interesting but also upsetting part is that children are not taught masking but rather start masking on their own.

Camouflaging

The below analysis, cited in the referencing section, was summarized by Rachel Worsley of Reframing Autism, which is a non-profit organization that does incredible work in the field of autistic studies and education. Worsley gives a stripped-down version of an academic investigation in wording that is relatable and understandable to non-academic parents and teachers. The research was conducted in the form of interviews involving seventeen autistic adults. Each participant had filmed conversations with a complete stranger and, at a later stage, had a loosely structured interview while watching the videos of the discussions. The idea was to get an understanding of camouflaging as identified by the "camouflager" so as to guarantee the accuracy of the exercise.

Definition of Camouflage:

For the purposes of the study, camouflaging was described as "the dynamic process through which autistic individuals modify their innate autistic social behavior to adapt to, cope within, and/or influence the predominantly neurotypical social environment" (Cook, J. et al, 2022).

The Findings

Thirty-eight different camouflaging behaviors were observed and split into four categories. Considering that there are so many camouflaging behaviors, it is no wonder that exhaustion, stress, and anxiety are possible results of camouflaging.

The four categories are:

- Masking: In this sense, masking was avoided; participants were reluctant to talk about themselves in any personal detail, even when it came to hobbies or general daily activities. Suppression of self-stimming behavior was noticeable, and during the post-stranger discussion interviews, it was apparent that some of the autistic individuals did not disclose their autism.

- Innocuous Engagement: Participants reported deflecting conversation away from themselves by apologizing for social faux pas or making excuses for behavior that was by no means problematic but just different. Other participants played down their intelligence or knowledge of their own areas of interest. There was a general theme of self-taught social conventions: Looking the stranger in the eyes, smiling, and laughing. The category being classified as innocuous is because the conversations lacked depth, not because the autistic individuals were afraid of depth but rather of how they would be perceived.

- Modeling Neurotypical Information: Tactics falling into this subsection included efforts to come across as neurotypical by displaying conventional hand gestures and other body languages, as well as slowing speech and aiming for clarity during discussions.

- Active Self-Preservation: Participants revealed that they created pre-planned topics of conversation that would open up channels of communication. During the discussions, there was a concerted effort to engage in equal amounts of talking and listening.

Importance of the Study

Academic studies should be regular and progressive. This study was the first of its kind, and the knowledge that was obtained is a resource or tool that can be used to assist autistic individuals in shedding the need to mask. The more that is known about a subject, the more that can be done to address the practicalities of the subject.

Self-Stimulating Behavior in Masking and Camouflaging

Clapping one's hands versus flapping with one's hands is an example of how some autistics may mask their natural, innate desire to exhibit self-stimulatory behavior. They are attempting to self-stim less, or in a more acceptable way, to appear more neurotypical. Many autistics may attempt to mask their emotions by not expressing them physically, so they don't jump or pace repeatedly to show their happiness as their bodies are naturally inclined to do. Avoiding self-talk or social situations altogether are other examples of masking self-stimulatory behavior.

What Is Double Empathy?

Dr. Damian Milton's double empathy theory is one that succinctly explains the disparities between autistic and non-autistic people. It also highlights the way in which society displays prejudice, sometimes unknowingly, towards autistic individuals (Milton, D., 2018). Dr. Milton has been recognized for several years through his lecturing career at the University of Kent. He is also an author, the chair of the Participatory Autism Research Collective, and, of course, the force behind the double empathy theory.

The theory puts forward the idea that one group always finds it difficult to put themselves in another group's shoes or attach themselves to another group's experiences by virtue of the fact that such experiences are different. As a result, empathizing with each other is difficult, perhaps impossible. Applied to autism, and as we know, autistic children display and experience emotions differently, as well as communication, relationships, and general world experience. Autistic individuals can lack insight into neurotypical behavior and vice versa, meaning that non-autistic individuals often struggle to empathize with neurodivergent people. It is basically a case of incorrect interpretation or a lack of mutual insight, which creates what is known as "the empathy gap."

Non-autistic communication and empathy tools are typical, whereas the atypical presentation of communication and empathy is different and often labeled as wrong or incorrect. Even though the empathy gap is experienced by neurotypical and neurodivergent groups, there is inequality in terms of the way that empathy is felt in both groups. The assumption is that the non-autistic communication and empathy method represents the correct way to engage. It is obvious that this assumption is prejudicial to autistic people and their communicative and empathetic behaviors. There is thus a misconception that autistic people are just people with broken parts to their disposition or personality.

Due to this misconception, there is a social expectation that autistic people must fix their broken parts so that they can behave and interact like non-autistic people. Unfortunately, traditional therapy, which has become outdated and is frankly archaic, has used the reward system, in which an autistic child is coached into behaving non-autistically in exchange for a reward. The converse is the idea that punishment must be inflicted on autistic children when they are simply being themselves.

The unfair part is that autistic children are expected by larger society to act as if they are not autistic, and no effort is made to understand that the separation is a difference, not a problem. The same does not apply to non-autistic people, to whom society does not dictate in terms of adopting autistic behavior. Neither group can empathize with the other, but one group is expected to do so, which is simply not possible. In crude terms, and this is a generalization, non-autistic people do not care about autistic people and are not prepared to learn before criticizing or writing off autistic individuals.

Society is most certainly not inclusive, and this is the cause of the alienation, embarrassment, and isolation felt by autistic people. Bullying is common in children with autism, and the results can be tragic, considering that suicide is very often seen in autistic people. Not catering to the habits, hobbies, requirements, and differences in the function of autistic children is a big problem, as the formative years shape the rest of a child's life.

Putting the Theory Into Practice

We can't be too critical of society, bearing in mind that autism is not widely understood, and that is one of the reasons why the double empathy theory seeks to change perceptions.

The National Autistic Society has developed training programs influenced by the theory, but much more application and education are needed. We must, however, take comfort in the fact that there are ways to change perceptions and dispel ignorance.

Authors Caren Zucker and John Donovan co-wrote a New York Times best-selling book turned PBS documentary titled *In a Different Key*. The story reveals the tale of a reporter and the mother of a young Autistic adult son who tracked down the first person ever diagnosed with autism in the US. What she learns during her journey teaches her and the viewers an immense amount, some of which is surprising and pleasing and some of which is disheartening. In the end, the documentary leaves the viewer hopeful that society is capable of change and that we should support those individuals that may appear different from us.

Socials Skills Learning for Children

Social skills change as a child grows up. Like any person in this world, we all have strengths and weaknesses. As a very simple example, some people are good musicians; others are not but can still learn to play an instrument. In the realm of social skills, autistic children are no different. Just like teaching someone to play a musical instrument, where fluency and change of method are necessitated by progress, teaching social skills to autistic children will also change depending on the situation.

The idea is to reach a point where social skill displays become automatic. If an autistic child is working on a goal related to learning how to compromise in their relationship with peers, frustration might creep in initially. When all the nuances of how to compromise and the benefits of compromise are understood, then some real progress has been made.

Teaching social skills can be developed through games. If emotion identification is being worked on, the autistic child could be asked to call out different emotions based on picture cards. After thirty seconds, the parent or educator will pause and count the picture cards together with the child. Each time the exercise is repeated, the incentive of beating the previous score should be enough to provide fun and excitement, which is conducive to effective learning.

Without losing sight of the fact that autistic children do learn in different ways, this method is applicable to anyone. Just some of the possible goals for social skills learning are:

- Thinking in a flexible way.

- Knowing when to say what's on our minds versus when we should hold the thought in our heads.

- Understanding the concept of reading a room.

- Understanding how to adapt the how, what, and why we communicate, depending on the situation we are in or the person we are talking to.

- Understanding how and why we compromise in friendship, or at work.

- Knowing how much information to share.

- Knowing about proximity expectations.

- Understanding/using tone of voice.

Chapter 4:

What Does Socializing Mean to

Neurodivergent Individuals

Many neurodivergent individuals, whether children, teens, or adults, prefer spending time with other neurodivergents. This *thinking* also applies to neurotypicals, in that like-minded people gravitate towards each other. The result is that our friends have similar interests, are probably close in age, and are people by whom we do not feel judged. Autistic individuals are inclined not to feel judged when they interact with other autistic individuals, as that sense of alienation is not present. It does not mean that neurodivergents and neurotypicals cannot be friends. Logically, parents spend time with their autistic children, and so do educators. Those are not strictly friendships but do constitute interactions between neurotypicals and neurodivergents.

Social Thinking © Methodology

Our human brains are automatically wired to think socially. We try to make sense of our surroundings and what is going on, as per our social radar. From that point, we can figure out what to do or how to act. Our social brain works all the time, even if we are reading, watching movies, or even just observing people in a general situation without interacting. Cognition or cognitive skills can be used to understand social thinking, and three broad categories, which overlap slightly, are used to group and understand the broader concept of social thinking.

A well-respected expert on the topic is Michelle Garcia Winner, who created a company by the name of Social Thinking © over twenty-five years ago. She has contributed to several best-selling books and provides online, and in-person training about the intricacies of social interactions, the importance thereof, and the skills to develop in order to improve social and general quality of life.

Michelle defines social thinking as:

"The ability to consider your own and others' thoughts, emotions, beliefs, intentions, and knowledge to help interpret and respond to the information in your mind, and possibly through your social behavioral interactions."

The Social Thinking © Competency Model strives to teach skills via language-based metacognitive tools to help both the interventionist and the student learning. The core vocabulary used makes some concepts that are somewhat abstract seem clearer, especially when paired with great visuals. These concepts include but are not limited to flexible thinking, just me versus you thinking, social detective thinking, and thinking with your eyes, body, and brain in the group. Teaching these concepts in real-time allows for increased self-awareness and better self-monitoring for the child.

Our Meaning Maker

As the name suggests, we make meaning out of life, not in the sense of answering the big life questions, but by observing and taking in our surroundings. Loosely, you could term it "assessing what is going on." To use a rudimentary example, when crossing a road, we look for cars, and when it is safe, we walk to the other side. This isn't a social setting in terms of conversations or interactions, but it illustrates the meaning we make out of the situation. Imagination is also a convention of our meaning makers, and autistic children can struggle in group interactions at school to listen to what the educator is saying, imagine or interpret it, then put it into action.

Adaptation of Social Behavior

For example, let's take a discussion between a thirty-year-old and an eighty-year-old. The discussion will be socially different from a chat between two thirty-year-olds. The younger person would talk slowly, explain concepts simply, use less slang, and tailor the conversation to the participants. The concept goes deeper than that, though, in the worlds of neurotypicals and neurodivergents; the three important "S-words" are: self-awareness, self-monitoring, and self-control.

Social behavior is about adapting to situations. In life, there are interrupters, including autistic children, but we can learn to hear the other person out before speaking. As a brief aside, it is interesting that neurodivergents and neurotypicals make exactly the same social faux pas, even though the social experience can be very differently experienced.

Using Social Skills

We all want to feel included and liked by friends, family, and even strangers, which means that employing social skills in a way that serves ourselves and others is important. It can be challenging for autistic children to understand how to give the other person or people the desired emotional experience. Due to this, autistic children may be perceived as anti-social or self-absorbed when, in fact, they are just displaying differences. At the end of the day, social skills are taught to most children; some are better at socializing than others, but with constant teaching, autistic children can thrive in social settings that may have seemed overwhelming in the beginning.

What Exactly Are Social Skills?

We could probably create an exhaustive list of what social skills actually are. However, in a broad sense, the following five categorizations can be seen as umbrella terms under which the larger scope of skills fall:

- Social awareness

- Social cognition

- Social communication

- Social motivation

- Autistic mannerisms

As we know, neurodivergents interpret the world differently, and the old-fashioned thinking that autistic individuals lack social skills is outdated and incorrect.

Social "Norms" and Cues

Having a quick conversation with a server when ordering coffee will probably go something like this:

Server: Good morning; how are you?

Customer: I'm fine, thanks. May I please have a medium coffee with extra cream?

Server: Yes, sure.

Customer: Thank you, and have a nice day.

Server: You too.

In this scenario, when the customer is asked how they are doing, they don't go into details about their work issues or their recent holiday. The exchange is quick, polite, and pretty generic. An autistic person in that situation may start telling the server their life story, and it makes perfect sense. The server asks the question, so the autistic individual answers it, but the social norm is generally a quick, polite, frivolous exchange.

Take a scenario where an autistic person is on a bus next to a stranger, and the stranger strikes up a conversation. Perhaps the stranger says, "Tell me about yourself." That is a social cue that informs the autistic person that he or she may talk about themselves. The polite thing to do would be to finish answering the question and then ask it back to the other person. That skill can be taught by explaining that a conversation should flow both ways and that this type of interaction is vastly different from the server example.

Sarcasm and Humor

Some people, neurotypical or neurodivergent, struggle with sarcasm, but using sarcasm can be a good icebreaker or a way of lightening the mood. Autistic children tend to be very literal and have trouble understanding sarcasm, which may create the impression of disinterest or irritability. Although not strictly sarcastic, the "Why did the chicken cross the road? To get to the other side" (joke). If interpreted literally, is not funny at all. An autistic child will probably think that it is stupid because it is logical.

Masking can also come into play, where a child learns to laugh at a certain point but hasn't actually identified the sarcasm. Some may argue that this is a good thing because the child will feel included. However, if the child is taught how sarcasm works, then there is a good chance that inclusion will be a result of understanding the use of sarcasm and actually enjoying the humor.

Manners

It is the responsibility of parents to teach their children manners, which can be challenging for autistic children. The school also plays a role, but we can't forget that if manners are not understood, it takes a lot more time and effort to learn them. This is another social convention that doesn't really separate neurotypicals and neurodivergents. Saying "please" and "thank you" are the very basics. However, you will often see parents constantly reminding their children to use those words. It is a very simple example, but the point is that repetition is a tool to be used with any child. The difficulty is that autistic children may miss the cues, but identifying when to stand up to greet somebody, open a door, or participate equally in a conversation, etc., are all teachable skills.

Back and Forth Conversation

During conversations, body language is used extensively, so not only talking but also conducting our body language is the correct way to suit the situation. Often, autistic children will shy away from talking, which can be perceived as a lack of interest. However, the reality is that an autistic child may feel overwhelmed in a conversation and, for that reason, exercise non-participation.

Initiating a Conversation

This can be practiced at home, and like anything, repetition is the key. Autistic children will often be interested in, perhaps even obsessed with, a specific area of interest. In the previously mentioned Netflix series, *Atypical*, the lead protagonist has a fascination with penguins and their Antarctic environment. He reads about them, draws them, and brings them up often in conversation. As an autistic boy in his late teens, it is fantastic that he has a subject that he loves talking about. However, the other person in the conversation may want to talk about different things, which is the way that a back-and-forth discussion should play out.

There are five main conversational skills, among others, that can be developed when working with an autistic child to prepare them for real-world conversations:

- Picking a topic
- Starting the dialogue
- Taking turns to speak
- Asking questions and answering questions
- Ending the conversation at the right point

In a role-play situation, the autistic child must pick a topic that they are interested in. As it is an accurate example, I will use the interest in penguins from *Atypical*. This is not an actual conversation but a hypothetical one. ND refers to neurodiverse, and NT refers to neurotypical:

ND initiates a conversation with a new child at school.

ND: Hello, my name is ND. What is your name?

NT: My name is NT; nice to meet you.

ND: Nice to meet you too. Do you like penguins?

NT: I don't really know much about them.

ND: Would you like me to tell you about them?

NT: Yes, if you would like to.

*ND talks for a few minutes on penguins; an appropriate amount of time.

ND: Do you like any animals?

NT: Yes, my family actually has a small farm.

*NT talks for an appropriate time.

ND: I would like to excuse myself, please. I have a class to get to. It was nice talking to you.

NT: Yes, it was nice talking to you. Maybe we can talk more tomorrow.

ND: I'd like that.

The above is a very summarized version of a role-play exercise, with the goal of limiting the amount of time that the autistic child spends on their area of interest and giving the other party an equal amount of time to speak about their interest. The open-ended questions promote the flow of the conversation. Politeness and ending the conversation at the right time are also part of the exercise. These types of role-plays can then be applied in the outside world and assist in developing mutual friendships that are a component of a better quality of life.

Visual tools and cues, such as a drawing that shows the child how much to add to a conversation (a ruler or measuring cup would be an appropriate representation) visuals to help a child know when and how to change the subject when to pause, and when and how to ask follow-up questions (the stop and go of a traffic light would be a good visual representation). Getting a child to know the difference between. When to "say it" and when to "think it" can be taught by pairing photos of feeling faces with practice phrases such as "I hate your new haircut" paired with a photo of a surprised face.

Communication

As we all know, poor communication generally has poor results, whether in romantic relationships, work relationships, or relationships with friends. Sometimes, autistic children find it a challenge to put all the components of communication together, so manners may slip, or the mutuality of conversation may be forgotten.

Looking Directly at Others

Maintaining eye contact can be extremely stressful and anxiety-inducing for autistic children. It does not translate into not caring what the other person is saying, but it can inhibit picking up cues and reading the conversation. The jury is out on whether or not to teach autistic children to make eye contact because it may feel forced and will then be a major source of distress in a conversational environment. We look at a face for many reasons—there is INFORMATION in the eyes, eyebrows, and face overall. We "reference" for information, permission, and shared enjoyment. My neurotypical 6-month-old son saw a butterfly when he was looking out the window. He *referenced* me (by looking at me) to share the joy of his discovery, and because he couldn't speak at the time, I gave him the words with a smile: "Yes, you see the butterfly, and you want to see if mommy saw it too; I do see it!... It's flying in our yard."

There are a variety of "silent" games we can play that teach children they must look in order for the fun game to continue. During the lessons or games, we don't try to achieve eye contact by asking for eye contact or calling their name. A quick glance at the speaker is all that is required for the game to continue. We need to remember that when doing eye contact exercises, it is important to teach WHY eye contact is necessary. If there is a reason behind something, it will make more sense to put it into action.

Not Responding to Being Called

Being easily distracted or zoning out when being spoken to can appear rude, but many autistic children and adults, especially those with ADHD, sometimes don't even realize that someone is trying to get their attention. We have all been in a situation where we are engrossed in a book or completely focused on a TV show, and we don't hear or subconsciously block out our name being called. The same thing applies to autism and can happen mid-conversation. Active listening exercises are very helpful. In a mock conversation, you point out to your autistic child that they have allowed a distraction to creep in. To work on this, use very short bouts of conversation, take a break, throw a ball around for a few minutes, then go back to chatting. The result of our readiness for longer, engaging conversations will come very slowly, but it will come.

Parents often become confused when their toddler doesn't respond to their name, yet when they sing a familiar tune, the child turns around toward the source of the sound. One reason they may not be responding is that they need to know that their name represents who they are and that calling them means you want them to look at you. Another reason they don't refer to you when you call them could be that they are more motivated by what is happening around them (the environment) or inside them (sensory). Some toddlers have receptive language (understanding) like a 2–3-month-old child. That being said, music is processed in a different part of the brain than the part involved in language use or understanding.

Not Engaging in Small Talk

Small talk can be very generic and awkward at the best of times. Autistic children tend to find small talk boring and pointless, so this skill and the **reasons** behind it need to be taught. If you are in an elevator with someone, the atmosphere can feel uncomfortable, and short bits of conversation like "the weather is nice" or "did you have a good weekend?" can fill that awkward space. Just like the chicken crossing the road, an autistic child will very likely see this as an obvious and unnecessary statement. Role-playing to teach different types of small talk in differing environments is good preparation in terms of understanding and employing small talk when required.

Continuing to Talk About Something That Other Participants in the Conversation Are Not Interested in

Social conventions dictate that in conversations, we sometimes have to entertain a topic that the other person is talking about, even if we find it boring. Using social tact, we may want to change the subject and go about it in a way that fits the conversation, such as picking up on something specific, making a comment, and directing the discussion towards another topic. It is, however, easy to miss the social cues when we are talking about something that the other participant finds uninteresting. These types of social cues are important to developing a conversation that provides stimulation to everyone involved. I gave the earlier example of the neurodivergent character from the series *Atypical,* who has a love for everything penguin. Nature is something that many people find interesting, but if only one aspect or one animal is a continuous topic, it will get boring. For your autistic child, it is necessary to get the balance right. In role-playing conversations, let your child talk for too long on one topic, then stop him or her. Do the same when it is your turn to talk, and note when he or she starts to get bored. The more practice there is, the more understanding and comfortable discussions will become with peers.

Relationships

All of the social skills that we have dealt with come together in the development of relationships. Often, when we hear the word "relationship," we think of a romantic one, but as I mentioned earlier, relationships take many forms. I would highly recommend the Netflix series *Love on the Spectrum.* The show aims to show that autistic people are all different in terms of their abilities, likes, and desires in a relationship. It showcases their desire for connection and some of the obstacles they encounter along the way. Parents, friends, and educators that understand and assist autistic individuals are interviewed, and one really gets a sense of how much love and care goes around. We all need love and care! Let's take a look at non-romantic relationships for now.

Levels of Friendship

Friendships improve and enrich our lives, but it can be tough for autistic children to initiate long-standing friendships. If we are not sure of what a friendship actually is, then making friends maybe even more challenging. Teaching autistic children about friendship and allowing them to understand the different levels of friendship gives them a practical sense of what it means to be friends with someone. Take social media, for example: Many people have thousands of Facebook friends but only talk to a fraction of those people. Often, we meet someone once, receive a friend request, accept it, and never talk to that "friend." That doesn't translate well into real-life, face-to-face friendships, but there are four commonly regarded levels of friendship. If an autistic children can be taught the differences, then they can identify what friendship means to the other person and what level of friendship can be attained.

The book *Why Johnny doesn't flap: NT (neurotypical) is OK* by Clay, and Gail Morton features an autistic child narrating his thoughts and feelings about his neurotypical friend's odd behavior, such as *not flapping* to show excitement to the audience. It's a book all about perspective… I love it! We need more books like this, and they need to be read to *all* children in *all* classes.

Acquaintances

People can have several acquaintances; a neighbor is an often-used example. You may know your neighbor's name and what work he or she does, but aside from polite exchanges when you happen to see each other over the fence, you don't engage in lengthy conversations. The same could be said for interactions with the library clerk or the lifeguard at a local pool—anyone with whom you have a very small amount of small talk on semi-regular occasions.

Casual Friends

Casual friends are more than acquaintances, and the obvious difference is that casual friends make plans to meet as opposed to just having a conversation if and when they run into each other. Casual friends may enjoy going to see a movie together or playing catch at the park. Usually, there is a shared interest, let's say hiking, around which the friendship is based. Discussions are likely to be limited in a "personal life" sense, and a casual friend is someone that you would probably not share about the intricacies of your problems or issues. It could be argued that most close friendships start out as casual friendships and grow from there, but of course, some casual friendships remain that way without evolving.

Close Friends

Close friends will probably see each other more often and know a great deal about each other. Emotional support, guidance, and advice are all characteristics of a close friendship. You feel comfortable enough with that person to share a lot of information about yourself, your life, other relationships, and vice versa. There is no specific amount of time that needs to pass in order to become close friends with someone, but it comes down to the frequency of interaction.

Here are a few more characteristics of what one would call a close friendship:

- You are happy to help and want to help each other.
- You do not fear judgment when asking for advice.
- You respect and appreciate each other.
- You do not feel a need to mask or camouflage.
- You empathize rather than criticize.

Intimate Friends

An intimate friendship is only a slight step up from a close friendship. All the same tenets as above apply, but essentially, there is no topic too sensitive or intimate to discuss. Intimate friends feel completely safe in each other's company and want to spend as much time as possible together. An intimate friend is a best friend, and yes, one can have more than one best friend.

Friendships in Autism

The friendship levels are the same for everyone. However, for autistic children, the ability to identify what information to share, what to say, and how to say it are the difficult parts, as explored in the social skills section. Nobody enjoys rejection, which is a real fear in any potential relationship, and as is the case with autistic children, alienation is a possibility.

Encouraging friendships between neurodivergents and neurotypicals is a double-edged sword, largely because neurotypicals can have a limited understanding of the differences, especially the fact that the initial stages of a relationship can be scary for neurodivergents. There are ways to slowly integrate and take a relationship from an acquaintance to an intimate friend, but it has to be treated delicately. One of the ways in which friendships can be formed is through sports.

Such is based on a mutual interest as well as the inclusive feeling of working together to score a goal or make a touchdown. For example: Any shared interest, like art, music, or video games, works to begin a friendship. More education needs to happen in schools so that neurotypicals are more patient, kind, and understanding. Kids are not weird if they aren't "just like you."

I also like the idea of neurodivergents befriending other neurodivergents as well. This dynamic works especially well for the parent, as it takes a lot less stress off them to sit and chat with another mom, knowing if their child does something *unexpected*, it wouldn't be too big of a deal.

Sports and Autism

Even though team sports provide a way to engage positively with other autistic children, the fear of letting a teammate down or playing badly might be present. Individual sports can also be daunting, but the improvement and application of social skills can be achieved. In terms of the most popular sports that autistic children enjoy, team sports, in general, come in fourth place, so there appears to be a propensity to favor individual sports in a group setting. Here are the top three:

Swimming

Studies have shown that swimming is the number one preferred sport for autistic children. Apart from health benefits, swimming is of great assistance in improving gross motor control in autistic children.

Horseback Riding

First off, equine therapy can teach autistic children to form connections with animals. If one struggles with human relationships, developing a bond with a horse, for instance, can educate an autistic child as to the way relationships feel. Like all sports, there is a fitness element, and being outside can't do any harm.

Martial Arts

Martial arts is about discipline, and as we know, autistic children often like specific rules as well. A 2019 study, referenced below, found that after a thirteen-week mixed martial arts program, autistic children of school-going age showed large improvements in self-regulation, focus, and attention (Phung, J. Goldberg, W., 2019).

Appropriate Reactions

As I have said before, social conventions tell us how to react appropriately in different contexts. Very often, we do not comply with those social conventions, but we are aware that they are there. Raising one's voice in a discussion or failing to help someone in need are small examples. So, parents and educators need to explain to autistic children what the most productive reactions are in social settings that may be unpleasant, awkward, or unfounded.

Bullying and/or Rejection

Bullying appears to be on the rise and is something that most humans have dealt with in their lives. It also appears that when school bullies grow up and reach maturity levels, they often regret their actions. Being bullied can leave lasting emotional scars, and with maturity, victims of bullies very often fail to shake off the memories and the feelings associated with their former school bullies.

Dr. Lori Ernsperger, Ph.D., has been instrumental in addressing bullying and the ways in which it can be approached. She owns and runs Autism and Behavioral Consulting ©, and provides workshops for educators and parents, especially on the "three R's" to combat bullying:

Recognize

Parents and educators of autistic children are under no illusions that bullying is frequent but often not recognized. The "know it when you see it" mantra can be applied. However, children still need to be taught to recognize bullying. Getting into an argument with a friend is probably not bullying; being pushed around or harassed by a classmate is probably bullying. The intention is the thing to look out for.

Respond

Anyone who sees bullying taking place has the responsibility to act in the correct way. If a friend is being bullied, the primal reaction may be to beat up the bully, but as the saying goes, "two wrongs don't make a right." Everyone who is involved with children, from the school bus driver to the school principal to the hall monitors, needs to be aware of bullying. The next step, if you are unable to harness the bullying situation, is to report it.

Report

Educators are taught how to address bullying, and even as a parent, you should report bullying to teachers, therapists, or other persons who are there to act in the best interests of your autistic child. By way of a quick Google search, you can find many organizations and societies that assist with bullying prevention. There is no harm in reporting it to as many helping hands as possible as long as it is positively addressed.

Empathy and Autism

Empathy is the ability to identify with another person's situation and share the feelings that they are experiencing. Our ability to empathize is drawn largely from having felt what the other person is feeling before, also called "lived experiences." There was a school of thought, and perhaps there still is, that autistic individuals lack empathy. However, very often, the case is that *empathy* is not overtly obvious because such individuals do not know how to show it; that doesn't mean that it isn't there. This is merely a difference and not a problem or abnormality. In fact, it is believed that approximately 15% of people do not feel empathy at all (Hall, J. Leary, M.). In autistic children, role play is an excellent method of teaching the ways in which to show empathy through listening, talking, and physical contact. Sometimes a simple hug can go a long way toward illustrating empathy without words.

Chapter 5:

How to Use Words Constructively

Words are so powerful, and for far too long, terms such as "special needs," "high or low functioning," and "challenging behavior" have been used when referring to autistic and ADHD children. Humans should be kind to each other, and for that to work, we need to reassess the type of language we use to describe differences in individuals. One can effect change through language use, and it can be a slow process. Because alienating and insulting terms have been in use for so long, change does not happen immediately. Education must accompany change; if an individual uses language that they do not even know is negative and unproductive, then a change will never take place. In this chapter, we will look at language and the problems with certain terms, and expand upon the outdated versus the new.

High-Functioning and Low-Functioning

These categorizations are not medical terms and are, to a certain extent, self-explanatory. If we change the context completely, take a step back, and do a bit of analysis, we can refer to a "high-functioning or functional alcoholic." That would be someone who has a drinking problem but holds down a good job, maintains fitness, has healthy relationships, and operates as if they were not an alcoholic. Obviously, drinking too much is a big problem, but calling someone in that situation "high-functioning" is not offensive. Take someone who has the same problem with alcohol but is in and out of jobs, can't hold down relationships, and is not a positive asset to society. "Low-functioning" is an appropriate term, but don't forget that a person like this is causing low functionality themselves. In autism, it is merely a case of *differences*: different hobbies, different ways of expressing oneself, and different ways of interacting.

In life, people are good at some things and not so good at others. All it amounts to is being different.

The term "high functioning" can be problematic for some people. A former student of mine who is now an adult told me recently that because he was labeled high-functioning, many of his needs went unmet. He had a lot of sensory needs in the areas of vision and touch that were not addressed. This made his high school experience not just unpleasant but almost unbearable at times. Accommodations on his Individualized Educational Plan (IEP) could have quickly and easily made his life much more bearable.

High-Functioning Autism

That being said, self-advocating often falls on deaf ears, as general education teachers (another not-so-nice term) and exceptional student educators don't always have a good understanding of things like unregulated sensory systems and how significant they can be in everyday life. Let alone in a setting where learning is supposed to be taking place.

Although not the correct term, we need to explore it a bit. What follows are the characteristics of high-functioning autistic children. Some refer to them as "symptoms," but as we know, that is also not the correct term, so let's look at the characteristics that are shown by autistic children:

Routines

Following a specific routine is a good thing, and it is often observed that autistic children enjoy routines. For instance, waking up at a certain time, having the same thing for breakfast, always sitting in the same place, and watching only a few shows on TV. Just think of people who don't have routines and the stress that it can cause. One downside of a lack of routine is the struggle with punctuality. However, following the same or similar procedure every day allows for order to be maintained, which lends itself to experiencing less anxiety and feeling in control.

Specific Interests

For instance, if an autistic child is interested in dinosaurs, they will watch all the shows that they can find on dinosaurs, read books on the topic, chat about it often, have dinosaur toys, wear dinosaur clothes, and absorb themselves in everything dinosaur. There is often not a huge difference between neurodivergents and neurotypicals. For instance, children can become obsessive (in a good way) about learning a musical instrument, whether they are neurodiverse or not.

Food Habits

Autistic individuals often have very particular opinions and behaviors around food. This is sometimes linked to the desire for routine and consists of separating food on one's plate; veggies on this side, meat on that side, gravy in a bowl next to the plate, and so on. A reason behind this could be the different ways in which autistic individuals experience their senses. Avoiding foods with smells that are unpleasant or overwhelming, such as garlic, is a noticeable food habit, in addition to avoiding foods that are a particular color. The texture of food in one's mouth can play a big role in the acceptance or rejection of food, which could be why "neurodivergents" may prefer to only eat a few types of food.

Social Anxiety in Communicative Settings

This goes back to missing social cues and the distractions involved. However, as addressed earlier, role-playing and explanations of how to deal with social communication are tools that can be used to reduce anxiety.

Being Overwhelmed

Take a restaurant setting where knives are scraping plates, children are screeching, and music is being played. This type of combinational sensory overload can cause panic attacks or meltdowns facilitated by feelings of overwhelm. Alienation and feelings of being different in a negative way can follow, as well as stares from strangers and displays of judgment. We have to remember that being overwhelmed is so common in people, but the reaction is different in autistic children. We must also remember what overwhelm looks and feels like. When compared to neurotypical children, it can be quite different for autistic children.

Low-Functioning Autism

Like high-functioning autism, this is also not the correct term, but we still need to explore it a bit. Known nowadays as "level three autism," children require much more support from parents and educators. In this sense, autistic children may have trouble speaking and can be difficult to understand. Generally, the support needed involves reminding them—to put it colloquially—to brush their teeth, when to eat, and when to change clothes. Children who are level three autistic struggle with learning and will be unlikely to have a job as they progress through life, partially because social interactions are exceptionally intimidating. Like all children, they need love, care, and support.

Parents obviously need to be the advocates and voices for these children, taking into account the following high support needs:

- The need for vigilant supervision

- Non-speaking

- No interest in using AAC

- Does not point or sign during or after the toddler-aged years

- Does not imitate

- Permanent scars from self-injury

- Higher risk for abuse by strangers

- No concept of danger

- High elopement risk

- Sensory dysregulation

- Very little to zero self-care skills

- Disrobes regularly and/or unexpectedly

- Not toilet trained after the expected age

- Uses a bottle sippy cup after the expected age

The term "high support needs" is also a preferred term for "low-functioning." However, many parents fear the change in terminology as they are concerned about services (medical and therapeutic) not being available if we view ASD as "just a brain difference." Insurance companies won't pay for services if they are not perceived as medical.

Non-speaking doesn't mean non-thinking. Some non-speaking autistic adults are presented with AAC, such as an "alphabet letter board," and can suddenly communicate some pretty mind-blowing messages after decades of *silence*.

Levels of Autism

It is time to throw the terms "high-functioning" and "low-functioning" out of the window, as should be the case, and look at the three levels, the third of which we dealt with briefly above.

Level One

Otherwise known as the mildest form of autism and the one that we have discussed most in this book. This level of autism requires support, but to a limited degree, and is characterized by the following:

- Difficulty initiating social interactions

- Organization and planning challenges

- Missing social cues

Level Two

One could say this is the middle-of-the-road level and requires substantial parental and educational support, characterized by:

- Extreme focus on special interests

- Requiring the implementation of concrete rules

- Repetitive behaviors (talking about one subject excessively)

Level Three

This type of experience as an autistic child requires very substantial support, characterized by the following:

- Difficulties with communication, both verbal and nonverbal

- Experiencing greater distress in anxiety-inducing situations

- Rapid change of focus and/or activities

The autism spectrum is not linear, with level one at one end and level three at the other. Trying to describe it visually, the spectrum looks more like a web where traits occur on a continuum. A person could be highly verbal but have low sensory needs. They could also be non-speaking with a high need for routines. We should never assume anything at all regarding the intelligence of an autistic person, no matter their level.

Levels of support needs and cognitive abilities are not dependent variables.

Limitations of Autism Spectrum Disorder (Difference)

Imagine wanting to do something but just not being able to do it, and your brain does not allow you to execute the task. One can try to press through and then experience burnout. This happens to neurotypicals as well, but neurodivergents experience this phenomenon on a heightened level. ADHD individuals are particularly affected and will often get a task *almost* finished but can't quite complete it. Like any limitation, this can be overcome or at least managed. Don't forget that autistic and ADHD children have strengths and weaknesses in different areas. Some may need support at school but little or no support at home. The same applies to social interactions. If someone is aware of what limits them, that aspect can be worked on or managed to the point where such limitations become less and less prevalent.

Medical Model vs. Social Model

In a physical sense, the medical model sees a disability as a problem that the disabled person has. It is not seen as an issue for anyone but that person. In the case of a physical disability, let's say that we have someone who is paralyzed from the waist down and uses a wheelchair to get around. Stairs provide an obvious problem, and the medical model sees the "problem" as the wheelchair and not the stairs. In this model, the focus is on the paralysis and not the person and his or her differences.

The social model would see the steps as the barrier for the person in the wheelchair instead of seeing the wheelchair as the problem. If a person has different needs, whether physically or otherwise, the disability only comes into play when that person is excluded due to their differences. Removing difficulties faced due to differences is the responsibility of society, and this forms part of changing perceptions of autism and ADHD.

The medical model was conceived in 1951 by T. Parsons, and as one can imagine, back then, very little was known about autism. The model was more physically disability-focused and received criticism for the potential alienation of disabled individuals due to their "special needs" and the alienation that such individuals would feel. If one applies the model to autistic people, the word "disability" should not be used. In fact, the entire medical model should not be used, as autistic individuals are not disabled; they are just different in terms of their experiences and actions.

Shortcomings of the Medical Model

As noted above, the medical model is outdated and uses language that is neither constructive nor positive. It affects the way autistic children see themselves and has the potential to be a hindrance to positive development. Its shortcomings specific to autism and ADHD are:

- Giving a child and others the impression or belief that there is something wrong with the child.

- Creation of negative labels.

- The main focus becomes impairment, and the ordinary needs that the child has are deflected away.

- A sense of exclusion.

Positives of the Social Model

It is widely agreed that the social model is the most effective one that provides for positive growth by:

- Recognizing the child's value.

- Setting out barriers and solutions to overcome those barriers.

- Making the outcome the main focus.

- Nurturing relationships and needs every day.

- Creating a sense of inclusion.

Specialized Care

As a parent, your needs take a back seat when raising an autistic child, and in the early years, it can be hard to figure it all out. It can be difficult to know what to do or where to find educators and therapists who will cater to the needs of your autistic child. The IEP, or Individualized Education Plan, was designed to help parents of autistic children by giving them the extra support they needed. The Individualized Educational Plan, legislated by the US government, applies to the public school system. The early intervention (EI) program is available before a child is eligible for an IEP, from birth to the age of three.

THE INDIVIDUALIZED EDUCATIONAL PLAN

Some children qualify for an IEP as early as age three. As part of the pre-K–12 school system, an IEP lays out the special education instruction, supports, and services a student needs to thrive in school. The IEP can include both modifications and accommodations for kids with brain-based learning challenges. If your child qualifies for an IEP, remember that as a parent, you are part of the team of people who help develop the IEP. Your thoughts, opinions, questions, and concerns matter. Parents and IEP teams meet to flesh out a plan to provide support best suited to the child. As a parent, you can't quite tell the IEP team what to do, but there is a framework within which you can collaborate. IEP aims to be very inclusive (O'Shea, 2022).

Some examples of the many possible IEP accommodations:

- Reduced assignments and homework.

- Chunking of longer assignments.

- Preferential seating near the point of instruction.

- 50% additional time for tests and quizzes

- Noise-canceling for loud areas, such as hallways and lunchrooms.

- Warning and preparation when challenges are anticipated.

504 PLANS

In contrast to an IEP, which focuses on the educational benefits and often includes direct services such as speech or occupational therapy, the 504 Plan of the Federal Rehabilitation Act, ensures a student has equitable access to a learning environment. Accommodations of a 504 Plan are typically grouped into four categories: presentation, response, setting, and timing and scheduling.

Workshops

If an autistic child's classmates can gain information about autism and the reasons why neurotypicals and neurodivergents are different in disposition and experience, then inclusion is more achievable. There are so many opportunities to educate in this way, and it may be as simple as a parent or educator running a short workshop at an autistic child's school. With understanding comes inclusion, and as human beings, we should not criticize or pass judgment on things we don't understand.

High Sensory Needs

In a public or school situation, it can sometimes be a challenge to regulate different sensory needs, but there are ways to do so. Noise-canceling headphones for autistic children who are particularly sensitive to combinations of surrounding sounds have been shown to be effective. Monitoring odors in the classroom for less stressful smell experiences, wearing light-regulating glasses for reduction of heightened sensitivity to color or brightness, and controlling lunchtime meals for taste sensitivity treatment are all great ways of catering to the personal requirements of autistic children.

Self-Harm

Often in autistic children, self-harm is observed, but it is not about seeking out the pain but rather blocking out the overwhelming sensations created by sensory overload. Self-harm most certainly is not self-stimming, but the principle is similar, whereby a distraction is created as a coping mechanism for placement in an uncomfortable or anxiety-evoking setting. It is important to note that self-harm is always a result of something, and as we know, autistic individuals often also have mental health issues, such as depression. Cutting is often something that diagnosed depressives do to release emotional pain. However, cutting or other forms of self-harm could perhaps be categorized as mental illnesses themselves.

Self-harm has been observed in autistic children as a means of regulating sensory arousal. Most often, the intention is not to induce pain, and sometimes autistic children who seek out sensory arousal do not even realize that their actions, such as scratching themselves or hitting their heads against a wall, are pain-inducing activities.

A functional behavior assessment (FBA) should be conducted by a certified behavior analyst to determine the function and cause of the behavior (internal or environmental factors maintaining the behavior). During the process of developing an FBA, data is recorded, monitoring the antecedent (what occurs before the behavior) and the consequence (what occurs after the behavior). Once the results are analyzed, a behavior intervention plan (BIP) is written to change or improve the outcome for the student exhibiting the behavior judged to be harmful or causing injury.

Life Expectancy

Life expectancy in autism is affected by environmental and genetic risk factors. Unfortunately, long-term outcomes regarding independent living, education, and employment for autistic individuals do not lend themselves to a positive life expectancy. Autistic children are more susceptible to death as a result of physical injuries, and shockingly, the life expectancy of an autistic individual is only 39.5 to 58 years (Sala, R. et al, n.d.). Suffocation, asphyxiation, and drowning are three of the more common ways in which autistic individuals lose their lives.

In terms of drowning, anyone with an autistic child who lives anywhere near water (think pool, lake, canal) must consider teaching their child to swim, or at least to flip and float, when they are as young as possible (1–2 years of age). Since elopement is such a challenge for families, the risk of a child wandering into a body of water and drowning is real. It is the most common fatal injury among autistic children.

Suicide is reported to be higher among autistic individuals as opposed to neurotypicals. Taking one's own life is not a physical or medical condition, but considering that autism and mental health can be closely related, higher suicide rates are understandable. The tragedy is that the alienation and loneliness that are often imposed by society's treatment of autistic people are causes of depression, which in turn can lead to suicide.

In terms of general health, epilepsy is more common in people with autism, and epileptic seizures are a contributor to premature deaths. Heart disease and several intestinal ailments are further contributors. If we think about it logically, the stressors and near-constant presence of possible unpleasant situations causing extreme anxiety are not good for cognitive and physical health. Brain inflammation, strokes, and diabetes are collateral contributors to premature death in this sense as well.

The Puzzle Piece and the Infinity Symbol

The puzzle-piece symbol is definitely outdated and is considered offensive by many. This is not always the case, but there is broad agreement on the topic. The puzzle piece symbol was created by Gerald Gasson of the National Autistic Society (NAS) in the United Kingdom. The year was 1963, and a crying child was depicted next to the puzzle piece. NAS spokesperson Helen Allison was quoted as saying:

"The puzzle piece is so effective because it tells us something about autism: our children are handicapped by a puzzling condition; this isolates them from normal human contact, and they do not "fit in." The suggestion of a weeping child is a reminder that autistic people do suffer from their handicap." (Autisticalex, 2014).

Reading such a statement is very frustrating, but one has to remember that 1963 was a much less informed and much more ignorant time period. The designers, of course, were non-autistic individuals speaking on behalf of autistic individuals, but they were unaware of and not well-versed in the ins and outs of autism. The offense was not intended; however, as time passed, the reasons for the offense became clearer. Though many of their behaviors are initially not understandable to everyone, which could technically be looked at as "puzzling," the symbol is overall outdated and judged by many to be inappropriate.

Autistic people are not puzzles to be figured out, and that view needs to be banished.

The rainbow infinity symbol that represents neurodiversity and the golden-colored symbol for autism are much more appropriate. Surprisingly, they only became associated with autism in 2018. Popular opinion is that the symbol represents the diversity of the spectrum and of autistic individuals. In a sense, humanity can be represented by the infinity symbol, but it is particularly appropriate for neurodiverse and autistic people. It promotes the ideas of understanding, sharing, and the involvement of neurotypicals in supporting autistic individuals.

Is Autism Just a Neurotype?

The term "neuro" is a medical one that refers to nerves or the human nervous system, meaning that the term "neurotype" is a bit of a misnomer because type does not mean typical. It really isn't just semantics, as it may appear, because the word "typical" describes a person or thing with characteristics that are widely shared or most common in that grouping of people or things.

We know that the word "neurodiverse" is used in language about autism, but being neurodiverse does not necessarily mean that one is autistic. A child may have ADHD without being autistic but still, fit into the neurodiverse category. Other neurological differences make individuals neurodiverse. For example, consider tourette's, depression, schizophrenia, or dyslexia. Autism can present in conjunction with the examples, but being autistic does make someone a neurotype. Neurodiversity is the recognition of differences in the way in which autistic people experience life, but the term is not solely descriptive of autism.

We do need to recognize autism for what it is, and to illustrate that it is not just a neurotype, here is the definition as per the American Psychological Association (APA) definition:

"Autism Spectrum Disorder referred to any one of a group of disorders with an onset typically occurring during the preschool years and characterized by difficulties with social communication and social interaction and restricted and repetitive patterns in behaviors, interests, and activities."

Late Identification of ASD

Most autistic individuals are identified as children. However, there are cases of autistic individuals only being diagnosed as adults. If you think or suspect that you may be on the spectrum. you may indeed be autistic, but have very low support needs. However, your quality of life can be improved after being diagnosed in very similar ways to the support provided to autistic children, as discussed in this book.

There are signs that can be used as identifiers for autistic adults, for example:

- Finding it difficult to participate in conversations.

- Being unable to relate to other people's thoughts, words, and experiences.

- Making noises in situations or places where quiet is expected.

- Using the same tone and manner of speaking in every situation, whether vastly different or not.

- Struggling to form close or meaningful friendships.

The good thing about getting a diagnosis is that you can begin to understand yourself better, including the way you relate to the world. If you know why you react in this way or behave in this way, then you can work on measures to combat anxiety or discomfort. You can find support through groups, therapists, or family, with the ongoing goal of improving your quality of life. We all want the best quality of life possible, whether we are adults, children, neurodiverse, or neurotypical.

Chapter 6:

The Spectrum of Feelings

As a parent, when you receive a diagnosis and find out that your child is autistic, a variety of feelings may follow. It can be an up-and-down experience, with anger, validation, relief, confusion, and fear. Age, mindset, knowledge, and education will have an effect on how one responds to the diagnosis, but the hope is that the outcome is positive and allows parents to facilitate the support that their autistic child requires. In this chapter, we will look at ways in which to prepare for the diagnosis by delving into the different emotional experiences.

Receiving the Diagnosis

Although receiving a diagnosis is overwhelming, it is a good thing, but often there will be doubt as to the accuracy of the diagnosis. Your child is still your child after the diagnosis, so there is no actual change. However, knowing that your child is autistic should set the wheels in motion in terms of getting as much information as possible. Revealing the diagnosis to teachers, fellow parents, and family is a personal choice but highly recommended. This is a case of putting the focus on the "change of mindset," which is a big but achievable thing. You need to view the diagnosis as a positive starting point from which you can give your child the right kind of support and love that they need to have a good life. Everything becomes a learning opportunity, from crossing the road to having a polite discussion to practicing skills to alleviate anxiety-inducing experiences. The initial path forward from that line could be a difficult one, and there are a few largely recognized emotions that may follow.

Fear

Whether you are an adult who has just received a diagnosis or the parent of a newly identified autistic child, you may become scared. Questions like, "What now?" "Do I need to change/does my child need to change?" or "What will other people think?" may start flying around in your head, and you could have a notion of not knowing what to do. There is nothing wrong with this at all, and you can start to unpack everything, identify one fear at a time, and then address that fear before turning it into something positive, which needs positive action. You can look at it as if you were walking into a pitch-dark room and were afraid of what might be inside. When you put the light on and discover that there is nothing in the room to be fearful of, your fear is now baseless. So, shine some light on your fear(s) and move forward.

Relief

When you find answers to questions you have been asking about why your child is out of sorts, throws what people perceive as tantrums, or is highly sensitive in seemingly innocuous settings, a huge sense of relief is a possibility. Receiving a diagnosis that your child is autistic provides many answers to your questions and, again, is like a new starting point.

Disgust

This applies more to adults receiving their own diagnosis, and the reason is because of the negative stigma surrounding Autism Spectrum Disorder. You may have been called "strange" or "weird" when you were growing up, and getting diagnosed can trigger feelings that you are a strange or weird person. That is most certainly not the case; differences do not mean that there is something wrong with you. People diagnosed with depression often display disgust at themselves, and it is also stigma related. Unfortunately, human nature is to judge, and that includes judging ourselves, but in these cases, it is society's fault. As a parent of an autistic child, you may develop a "Why me?" or "Why my family?" attitude, and while this is understandable, it is not good, so if it happens, then try not to dwell on it for too long. To help with this, work on acknowledging that your life is going to be different. Feel those feelings and determine what it will take for you to be the best mom, dad, friend, and teacher you can be.

Regret

You may be inclined to look back and chastise yourself for having handled your child in a certain way, or that you would have done things differently had you known that your child was autistic a year or two prior. It's not your fault; you must move forward with your child's best interests at heart.

Acceptance

Acceptance will come, and when it does, the negative feelings and emotions will no longer exist. You can then pay clear attention to your child's support needs, acknowledge their strengths and weaknesses, do some real research, seek out help where you need it, and allow your child to live his or her best autistic life.

The ASD Grief Cycle

When we lose a loved one, we often hear about the grief cycle, which includes denial, anger, bargaining, depression, and acceptance. Some may argue that there are other stages, and while an autistic diagnosis does not bring on grief in the same way that it is brought on by a death—there can be grief uniquely associated with the identification of autism.

Shock and Disbelief

Receiving any news that may be perceived as bad can induce a knee-jerk reaction of shock and/or disbelief. Even if there has been an ongoing suspicion that there might be "something wrong" with your child, your attitude may be to question whether the diagnosis is correct. A symptom of shock and disbelief is becoming totally distracted while the doctor is explaining the intricacies of what the diagnosis actually means. You may experience self-contained panic as thoughts fly around in your head, leaving you unable to take in and process the information being conveyed.

Allow yourself to react in the way that you do; you can always see the doctor again. When you leave, don't self-judge. Let your body dictate your reaction. Isolate for a while if you need to, or surround yourself with friends and family. When calm descends, you can book another appointment and go in prepared with a list of questions and a positive disposition. Remember that there is no wrong, incorrect, or bad reaction. Just like your autistic child, reactions are different, that's all.

I'd like to address the sibling of the neurodivergent child. After a particularly rage-filled and exhausting morning over not being able to locate a hairbrush. My own son has asked me, "Why can't she just be normal?" My son's question made me so sad. I was sad for myself because I loved both my children, but I often found myself feeling anger, loss, jealousy, frustration, and even contempt when dealing with some of the unexpected anger outbursts from my daughter. Now I felt sorrow, guilt, loss, sadness, and discouragement for my son. At seven years old, he knew his friend's siblings were not this rageful. The temperament, age, gender, personality, and birth order of siblings make a difference in how they experience life with a neurodivergent brother or sister. Neurotypical siblings can have struggles, particularly with anxiety, depression, and social difficulties, so they should receive education and support.

Parents are encouraged to change their attitudes and the examples they set. Research by Debra Lobato found that siblings describing their own experiences consistently mentioned their parents' reactions, acceptance, and adjustment as the most significant influences on their experience of having a brother or sister with a disability (Lobato, 1990). It is also important to note from Lobato's research that a mother's mental and physical health is probably the most important factor in predicting sibling adjustment, regardless of the presence of disability in the family.

Denial

Denial is a more measured reaction than shock and the immediate thought that a mistake has been made with the diagnosis. That is why denial takes a bit more time, but it can provide the opportunity to get second opinions, which is completely understandable. A good tip is to use your denial positively and gather as much information as you can. Often, we know that we are in denial, and it is necessary to ride it out; denial will fade or could possibly just disappear when you come across a sign, have a discussion, or read something that brings acceptance. If you are aware of the denial, talk to a therapist to figure out what is behind it. Ultimately, as parents, we have to do what is best for ourselves, our children, and the entire family. We cannot do that if our denial prevents us from seeking the services our children need and deserve. They will grow up, and in any good parent's heart, we know we want their lives to be happy, so if our denial is preventing their success, growth, or happiness, we need to figure it out.

Anger or Rage

If denial does not quite get you to acceptance, anger or rage are likely to become your main emotions. There is a jealousy element as you question why this has not happened to another family or another child. You may wonder why people with children whose parents are bad to have happy, healthy kids when your parenting is much more loving and nurturing. Your anger could be directed at your spouse, your autistic child, or their siblings. That is the nature of anger: It is easily misdirected and can become all-consuming to the point where you live in your own head and fail to notice how you are affecting people at whom you lash out. Many people see anger as a bad thing, and to a degree, it is. However, we have to allow ourselves to feel that anger, but we also need to control it and not let it hurt the people we love. A tip extracted from Cognitive

Behavior Therapy is to write things down: your feelings, your mindset, and your manifestation of anger. Writing may help!

Confusion and Powerlessness

As the saying goes, knowledge is power, and in the early stages, you will know very little about autism. What you do know is probably ill-informed by society's misinterpretations, so don't beat yourself up if you have misconceptions about autism being a disease or a mental disorder. The terminology will be new, but you will learn. Just be cautious about believing everything that you read or watch. Read academic studies or articles on well-established sites and ask lots of questions in order to alleviate confusion and take back power and control.

Depression

Powerlessness is one thing, but hopelessness is another. It is common for parents to make a premature decision to give up, thinking that they do not have the skills to parent an autistic child effectively. A parent can get consumed with thoughts of how the plan went wrong. The perfect family and white picket fence were the dreams, but now the family is strained, both financially and emotionally, carrying an unfair burden and feeling extreme despair. There is no easy fix for depression, but the very first step is to seek out a counselor, therapist, or psychologist. Also, you still need to live for yourself, so take time out to treat yourself and do the things that bring you enjoyment.

Acceptance or Not?

George Orwell, the British novelist, is quoted as having said, "Happiness can exist only in acceptance."

He is correct, and as human beings, we have faults, we do the wrong things, and we hurt others. Sometimes we do so on purpose, and other times by mistake. Either way, we need to accept our faults, acknowledge our mistakes, and feel the associated emotions before moving forward. Acceptance of a diagnosis of autism is no different, but we also have to accept the reality that happiness is never permanent. There are bumps along the road; when the diagnosis is received, things will get tough. However, there will be wonderful, exciting, fun, and happy times too. Accepting the diagnosis leads to understanding and presents an opportunity to educate others, work on yourself as a parent, and tailor your parenting to cater to and support your autistic child without neglecting other loved ones. Look at acceptance as a call to action, which includes finding answers and creating empowerment in supporting your child.

What to Remember

You have your child's diagnosis, and you are experiencing this whirlwind of emotions, but what do you actually do with the diagnosis and all the collateral that it brings? The answer involves thought and action. Here are five quick tips for the effective, positive forward motion:

- Take a deep breath.

- Don't ever think that you are alone.

- Educate yourself on ASD and treatment options.

- Practice acceptance.

- Remember to connect with others who are in similar situations via groups, social media, etc.

What Does It Mean for Your Family?

You may have a spouse or partner and two children. Perhaps one of your children is autistic, and the other is not. You don't want either of your children to feel as though they are not getting enough love or attention. However, just like autism means differences, there are general differences between children in age, gender, interests, and emotions. No two children are the same, and no two children require exactly the same support. Having said that, supporting an autistic child can be time-consuming, to the point where your other child or even spouse feels left out or that you, as a parent or spouse, don't care as much. Communication is absolutely vital, and if your family can sit down every single evening and discuss the day with absolute honesty, then feelings of equal treatment, love, and support can be maintained. Communication! Communication! Communication!

Isolation and Special Treatment

Nobody enjoys the feeling of isolation, and you don't want anyone that you love to experience it. It can be tricky with one neurodivergent child and one neurotypical child, which is why everyone needs to feel equal involvement. Parents living their whole lives for their autistic children is common, and there is a tendency to be overprotective. In such cases, it may be your neurotypical child who experiences it. Spouses can also become isolated from each other due to feelings of distance created by not feeding the spousal relationship adequately. Your identity should not be as a family with an autistic child but rather as a family whose children have different needs and different support requirements. Also, remember that siblings argue, and even have physical fights, and sometimes it is just about growing up. You don't want to instill in your neurotypical-minded child that he or she cannot get angry with your autistic child or, on the other end, cannot tease sarcastically, for example. Shielding a young autistic person from real life is an easy thing to do, but life is not an easy gambit, and it is the job of parents, but also educators, to allow all children to experience life.

Children need to learn right from wrong. To take a small example, if you borrow something, you should return it in the same condition in which you received it. This is highly hypothetical, but let's say one of your children borrows a book from the other. When your child returns the book, there is a coffee stain on the cover, which wasn't there before. Obviously, it was a mistake, and you need to let your child, whether autistic or neurotypical, get upset with your other child. You can't prevent a confrontation because one of the two children is autistic. These are the types of learning experiences that children and young teens go through. As long as both children feel equally treated, you have achieved your goal, and as I said before, communication is vital, so if your children feel unequally treated, you need to discuss it as a family.

It also comes down to special treatment, which is essentially an isolation-creating endeavor in any case. Treatment must be different, not special; take small things like turns washing the dishes. You don't want to be saying, "Shame, he/she is autistic, so let's let him/her off on the chores." That is special treatment. Parenting is a rocky road, but maintaining fairness and equal treatment, but by different means, is the best way to approach it.

Pay Attention to Other Stories

Never forget that you are not the first parent or family to have an autistic member, and there are many people with stories to tell. Talking and exchanging experiences can be empowering, which is why meeting with people who have autistic stories is a great way to feel heard and to give the courtesy of listening. What follows are explanations of two pieces of writing by Emily Perl Kingsley and Susan Rsuzidlo, fully referenced in the references section. They are interrelated as well as informative, but like anything, they have both garnered criticism, and rightly so.

Welcome to Holland ©

Some call it a poem; others call it an essay. Whichever category you put it in, Welcome to Holland © is Emily Perl Kingsley's take on not getting what you expected. She wrote the piece in 1987, and the message was a response to being frequently asked what it is like to raise a child with a disability. I mentioned 1987 for a reason, and that is because terms like "special needs" or "disability" have become outdated. In fact, Kingsley doesn't initially specify a diagnosis or condition but rather that her child has a disability before she begins to answer the question.

She talks about how the preparation for and excitement of having a baby are like preparing for and getting excited about a trip to Italy for an amazing holiday. However, when you touch down, you realize that you are actually in Holland, as the planning goes out the window and the disappointment descends. Kingsley goes on to suggest that, as calm sets in, the realization is that Holland is still a beautiful place. However, all the guidebooks, maps, and dictionaries for Italy have to be discarded. Then comes the challenge of acquainting yourself with new books, maps, and dictionaries. Basically, discarding what you had educated yourself on and planned for and learning something completely new.

Kingsley ends the novel in a heartbreaking way that may evoke thoughts of insensitivity and lack of acceptance. She talks about all the other people that successfully got to Italy and the stories that they tell when they return home. That was supposed to be the plan, but the pain of never having arrived never goes away. The last line is particularly poignant, and I will quote directly (Kingsley, EP., 1987):

"But… if you spend your life mourning the fact that you didn't get to Italy, you may never be free to enjoy the very special, the very lovely things… about Holland."

A point that I have not yet mentioned is that Kingsley's son, the subject of her poem-turned-story, was born with Down syndrome thirteen years prior to its publication.

In a time of rife speculation, one could argue that Kingsley sees having a child with Down syndrome as missing out on something. I cannot say for sure, but if this is the case, then it is understandable that her piece of writing would leave many parents of children with Down syndrome very sad. It is a bit confusing, considering that Kingsley is a winner of multiple awards in media as well as Woman of the Year in 1983 in recognition of her volunteer activities. She has definitely done some excellent work, but her metaphor doesn't sit well. This can be applied to having an autistic child, but again, it doesn't seem very kind. Perhaps one can blame the times, but that shouldn't be the case.

Welcome to Beirut ©

Although this piece, often called a *Parody*, was penned in 1996, at that time, offensive and unkind words were still in mainstream use. Susan Rzucidlo is a naturopathic physician and author who has an autistic son. Some find her work inspiring, but as with Emily Perl Kingsley's, *Welcome to Holland*, criticism has been leveled.

The piece of writing is humorous in some parts, and Rzucidlo starts off by referring to a situation where parents or a parent are content with life. They have two children, one of whom is different, as is the case with siblings. She then describes the "terrorist kidnapping scene," often aired in popular media. The bag over the head kicks in the stomach, getting driven somewhere mysterious. She likes the experience of the day on which parents receive the diagnosis stating that their child is autistic.

Beirut is, of course, a war zone, and Rzucidlo uses bombs and bullets as metaphors for the terms that one starts to hear post-diagnosis. "Lifelong," "neurologically impaired," "refrigerator mother," "a good smack is all he needs." Next comes the freakout, especially because nothing has changed except a label. It sounds strange to say, "My child is autistic." You have zero knowledge of autism, and you don't know what to do. Being a lab rat is likened to case workers being assigned; although it is interesting that Rzucidlo refers to herself as the lab rat, the thinking is understandable.

She goes on, saying that you get hit by bombs, and this is where she starts getting kinder, with the example of her child being bullied and the heartache that it causes. The exclusion and isolation, not only of an autistic child but also of the parents, is the next topic, as are medical insurance companies that only care about money. We all know that, though.

Then Rzucidlo abandons the war zone idea and talks of the kindness that other people show. It is out there, like a neurotypical sticking up for an autistic child on the playground. Maybe an educator, a therapist, or a friend empathizes and explains the sensory overload that can be experienced. When your autistic child struggles in a social setting and displays attention-drawing behavior, someone offers a kind smile with an unspoken assurance that they understand. She quickly reverts back to the war, saying that it is awful, but there are lulls in the bombs and bullets. However, she signs off in a caring way, talking about how amazing the good times are. Her last two sentences make visceral sense, as she writes, "Life is good, but your life is never normal. Hey, what fun is normal."

The Message

This book is not about criticism; it is about awareness, changing views, recognizing differences, supporting needs, kindness, hope, and love. It is understandable that there may be sections of Welcome to Holland and Welcome to Beirut that seem objectionable. Metaphors are a good way to explain things, though. My advice is to understand the lessons and takeaway points that the metaphors illustrate. Discard the negativity, hold on to the positivity, and create an environment that promotes equal treatment for your loved ones. Equal does not mean identical; different approaches promoting equality of outcomes are what you are aiming for.

Chapter 7:

Mindset Is Vital

If you go into a tennis match, to use an arbitrary example, and your mindset is that you are going to lose, you are halfway to that loss before you step onto the court. By way of another example, if you start learning the piano and your mindset is that you will never be good, then you are giving up before even giving yourself a chance. The same applies to your thought patterns and your focus on the positive rather than the negative. As I mentioned earlier, no person in the history of the world has walked through life without a single thing going wrong. On the days when things go wrong, and you feel like breaking down, just remember to get back to the correct mindset. A breakdown is fine as long as you acknowledge it, pick yourself up, and keep going. Stress is a reality, but it is an emotion or set of emotions that can be accentuated when raising autistic children.

Take It Day by Day

A commonly uttered phrase and a difficult mantra to live by, let alone implement. I don't mean that you shouldn't plan; planning is important, but know that the general plan will change from day to day. Children are people, just like adults, and they have different quirks. Teenagers can be disrespectful, autistic, or not. You don't know when your teenager is going to get argumentative and slam their door, but you know that it is bound to happen. On the day that it does, you already know how to deal with it; you were just not aware that it would happen on X-, Y-, or Z-day.

Learn to Manage, and Cater To Your Autistic Child's Differences

In any functional family, bearing in mind that the word "functional" could have many meanings, all members want to get to know each other well. If we know what our partner struggles with emotionally, we can be there for that person. Awareness is important, and as parents, you need to study your children. Not as in a scientific study but through observation, talking, and even trial and error exercises. Hypothetically, your autistic child is particularly sensitive to sound, more so than other sensory experiences. As a parent, you are aware of this, meaning that you can mitigate the discomfort, stress, and anxiety that your child feels by encouraging them to use noise-canceling headphones for argument's sake.

Prior to diagnosis, you may have been in a position of ignorance about the spectrum, neurodivergents, and neurotypicals. When you get the diagnosis, the learning must begin, both about your child and about autism in general. Knowledge is power, and with knowledge comes action.

Autism Management and Teaching Self-Care

If we look purely at statistics from the 2017 study by Shenoy, MD. et al, entitled *Comprehensive Management of Autism: Current Evidence*, it appears that nutrition and traditional medicine have a 74% prevalence rate in autistic children (Shenoy et al., 2017).

Intensive behavioral therapy and educational therapy, from as early an age as possible, have proved effective in allowing for better sensory experiences, or at the very least, the management thereof. These terms may seem a bit scientific, but all they represent is the implementation of measures to best support your autistic child. Things like role-play exercises involving your autistic child in activities that acclimate him or her to managing stressors. Encouraging social interactions, coaching how to handle them, and basically doing everything you can to give your autistic child the tools to have the best quality of life possible.

Self-care is very important, and as autistic children reach their teens, hygiene habits may change. A list of morning routines is very useful in helping your autistic child do the basics. Brush teeth, use the bathroom, shower, dry off, brush hair, use deodorant, put on clean underwear, and head downstairs for breakfast. As before, autistic children and adults, for that matter, like routines and having the instructions on the back of the bathroom door or stuck to the mirror is a small thing that goes an incredibly long way to promoting self-care.

As a parent, you also need to care for yourself; hygiene, yes, but as an adult, you probably have that covered. Parenting is tiring; nobody would argue against that, so take time for yourself when you can. Allow yourself a break, but also have fun with your kids. Slow down when you can; go for a walk in nature, read a book, do the things you love, de-stress, take a deep breath, and put your mom or dad hat back on for the next parenting whirlwind.

Adjusting Your Own Limitations

The sky's the limit, as we hear so often, but as educators and parents, we need to take a more practical approach and refer to the Welcome to Holland and Welcome to Beirut pieces from the previous chapter. Both had a sense of feeling inadequate, not having faith that they could parent effectively, and basically imposing limitations before taking action.

On the other side of the coin, there are imitations that you just cannot get around. No person can jump over a house, and we take that as a given. In other words, a limitation that is completely unchangeable. There is no point in even trying. To go back to self-care as an example, your autistic child may forget to put deodorant on, but that is something that can be fixed by reminders or a list on the mirror. As a parent, you are not limited in that sense. The adjustment comes in when things get a bit more complicated, and it comes down to control. You can supervise, help, and prepare, but you cannot know completely what is going to happen during your child's day.

In the same breath, as a non-therapist parent, you do not have the same knowledge and education that your child's therapist does. It may sound a bit harsh to classify this as a limitation but look at it in the sense of a physical wound. Your child cuts his or her arm; you clean the wound, apply pressure, bandage it up, and do what you can to the limits of your ability. Then you take your child to the hospital to get stitches. The same applies to caring for and feeding your autistic child's needs, to which there is a limit. For these reasons, therapy and tailored education are so important.

Coping With Negative Emotions

Negative emotions impact all of us, but some people manage them better than others. Many neurodiverse individuals cope with emotions better than neurotypicals, and emotional management is important not only for your child but for yourself as a parent. Identifying the source is the first step towards either eliminating the emotion or anticipating it in order to brace for it.

Let's look at resentment via a realistic scenario. As a parent of an autistic child, there is the real possibility of not being invited to social events due to the perception that your child is badly behaved or attention-seeking. The resulting resentment could be directed at your friends who do not invite you over anymore. Don't ignore the emotion; rather, track the source, or the cause, which is essentially the fact that your friends don't know anything about autism. Yes, there is an element of avoiding unpleasantness on their part, as in not inviting you in case your child becomes overwhelmed for whatever reason and has a panic attack. That is not your fault at all, but you also have to understand their position. From there, the best way is to talk; explain to them what autism is, what it means, and how your autistic child faces challenges that he or she deals with differently than neurotypicals.

The above sounds like a very easy method to apply, but it isn't. There are so many variables. Maybe your friends don't want to talk, or even if they do, their minds won't be changed. Perhaps they don't care about the reasons behind your child's actions in a way that they erroneously see as abnormal. You need to deal with emotions on a situational basis. Later in this chapter is a section on mindfulness, which will be very useful in learning emotion management tools.

While on the topic of resentment, you can't be blind to the possibility that you may feel resentment towards your autistic child for making your life and the lives of your family difficult or unpleasant. Feeling this type of resentment can then prompt guilt, followed by turning the resentment on yourself, and it is not unusual for depression to set in. Once again, you need to identify the source or cause. That little person is not at fault in any way at all, so the feeling is unfounded, but it is still present. If you acknowledge the above, then you can rationalize what is rational and begin to let go of the resentment.

In general, the human race is inherently negative, so coping can be incredibly difficult, whatever your circumstance or position in life. It is a step-by-step, day-by-day process that requires continuous work.

Understanding Your Child's Stressors

Like everyone else, autistic children experience positive and negative emotions. Just as a parent needs to identify the cause of their own emotions in order to manage them, that parent also needs to identify the causes of their autistic child's emotions, otherwise known as stressors.

We know that sensory experiences can be unpleasant and that a flickering light, a shirt label, or being overloaded by anxiety or panic-creating noises are stressors, but understanding them on a deeper level can help us to help our autistic children more effectively.

No Finite Set of Rules

As we know, autistic individuals like routines and going about daily tasks via a set of finite rules. An unexpected change in routine can be a major stressor. In a logical sense, a bus delay will cause stress to neurotypicals, so why should it not do the same to neurodiverse people? A person canceling a coffee meeting at the last minute can be a cause of irritation and stress, no matter who you are, but in autism, the stress manifests differently. Rules and schedules are often broken as nobody's fault, and it is the unpredictability that can be troubling. As a neurotypical parent, it is easy to understand from personal experiences that changes in plans cause stress. From that point, it becomes easier to understand the same stressor as experienced by autistic individuals.

Sensory Processing

As we know, autistic individuals process sensory information differently. However, if you compare yourself, as a neurotypical parent, to your autistic child, you will realize that your experiences are not "that" different. A flashlight being shined in your eye is going to cause distress; that is what it is like for an autistic child in what one may term a "normal light setting." The same principle is there for noises: If someone claps really loudly, right next to your ear, it is going to be unpleasant and stress- or anxiety-inducing. Your autistic child feels the same, but the clap is soft. So, in terms of sensory processing, you kind of start with the result, then move back to the cause, which is pretty much the same in autistic and neurotypical individuals. One could refer to it as the intensity of the sensory experience.

Social Situations

Although social interactions can be uncomfortable for neurodivergents, they can also be uncomfortable for neurotypicals. Similarly, to sensory processing, it is the intensity of the experience that marks the difference. In life, you get incredibly social individuals that will go to the park and ask to join a game of catch or touch football. For others, just the thought is a dreadful prospect. Social interactions are a double whammy, considering that sensory exposure also plays a part. You will remember the social stressor sections at the end of chapter three and the beginning of chapter four. When you understand the nature of the stressors, you can implement exercises, role-play, and home education.

Signs That Indicate the Existence of Stressors

The more you understand your autistic child and autism in general, the easier it becomes to identify when a stressor is being experienced or is approaching. You can then remove your child from that situation, and when he or she regains composure, you can give them praise.

A few examples of stressor indicators are:

- Uncomfortable hand movements

- Swaying back and forth

- Generally distressed demeanor

- Looking down

- Pacing or walking in circles

How Do Your Child's Stressors Affect You?

Because we love our children, we often feel their emotions along with them. Stress from any source can be debilitating, and constant worry about your autistic child is a source of stress. When you leave the house, you will probably be concerned that your child will encounter a stressor and have a breakdown. If you are at home and your child is out playing, you are likely to fear bullying, sensory stressors, or adverse reactions that others may not know how to deal with.

Unfortunately, statistics do show that 50% of mothers express a decreased enjoyment of life due to the stress of managing their family, including their autistic child (Boyd, 2002). Mothers and fathers provide support for their children and for each other. However, in order to be in the other 50%, support is needed from an outside source, such as a therapist or a therapy group.

Stress Management for Yourself

You need to be kind to yourself. Remember that exercise is a great stress reliever, largely because of the dopamine release. Also, if you are really exercising hard, you can't think deeply or over-analyze. Deep breathing and guided meditation are great sources of stress relief and fall under mindfulness, which I will get to shortly. Keeping a diary is an excellent way to de-stress. Go old school and write down your thoughts and feelings in an exercise book, not in a document on your computer. Personally, you might not be an "exerciser," or you may not enjoy writing; maybe you like swimming in the sea or reading fantasy novels. Do what works for you!

Mindfulness

You may have heard of Cognitive Behavioral Therapy (CBT), from which mindfulness is derived. They are not the same thing, but they do overlap and can be tremendously helpful in dealing with your emotions as a parent. Mindfulness techniques have been shown to be useful as part of therapy for autistic children. A semi-branch off is called Dialectic Behavioral Therapy (DBT). I am not going to go into the science and origins but rather explain how to apply a mixture of all three.

Parents/Adults

The first step is to acknowledge your emotions, which can be difficult. It is common to suppress our emotions or even ignore them. This leaves open the possibility of exploding one day and taking it out on others. The difficulties that you are having in your role as a parent can create frustration, anger, anxiety, stress, resentment, or a combination thereof. A good way to explain the next step is to describe it as an out-of-body experience, not in any supernatural way, but rather as a figurative backward step that allows you to look at your feelings and emotions in an objective way. I could compare it to standing directly in front of a painting. Everything is blurred, and you can't discern one color or depiction from the others. Take a few steps back, and the painting becomes clearer.

It is important to recognize where your anger came from, for instance. Perhaps you have been feeling that your partner has not been contributing equally to the household, emotionally or otherwise. You might start to feel bad because you haven't raised the issue, but that is okay. Now you need to remove self-judgment, which is a tough thing to do. Looking from a vantage point, you are allowed to forgive yourself. You then put yourself in a position to address the root cause. We do tend to catastrophize and think of the worst, but a simple discussion may reveal that your spouse or partner has been mentally distracted by a particular ongoing stressful work scenario. The next step is easy, sort of; you need to have a discussion and learn from the experience, which means you will know what to do the next time.

Another tenet of the trifecta is being acutely aware of your surroundings as you employ your senses to really focus on the seemingly mundane. This part of the technique acts as a distraction from the stress you may be carrying. Often, we rush around in the mornings: In and out of the shower, a quick brush of the teeth, getting changed in a hurry, whipping up a quick breakfast, and heading out the door. The sequence is not a stressor as such, but it does cause unnecessary stress and anxiety that can compound the longer-term emotions that we feel. Give yourself an extra half hour and take everything in—really feel the warm droplets in the shower. Pay attention to how they run down your back. Take time to enjoy the feeling; observe the texture of your toothbrush, and think of how amazing it is that we humans even have teeth. Pick out your clothes slowly, think how lucky you are to be able to eat breakfast, and use that thought to observe the different tastes. These types of deep observations can be applied all day. The name of the game is being present, which has great and holistic mental health benefits.

Guided meditation is similar, but it directs focus to your body as you lie down or sit in a comfortable chair with your eyes closed. Guided meditation can be combined with deep breathing, the observation of your chest moving up and down, your lungs filling with air, the slow release, and the calm that should descend. You can be attentive to your toes, wiggle them around, feel the sensations, and aim to be completely present. Thoughts will definitely pop into your head, but make it your goal to let them go and reset your focus. Ten minutes, three times a week, and you will improve your "being present" skills.

Children

The same general idea of mindfulness applies to autistic children, but it is much harder to embrace what is essentially something very different. Children might find it silly at first, but a slow introduction and continued mindfulness practice have shown to garner excellent results in understanding and managing stressors and reactions thereto. There is room for adaptability, and also for the parent or educator to become the guide where applicable.

Here are a few exercises to test out:

Sound Meditation

You can get creative with this one. Ask your child to lie down or sit comfortably and make a sound. Even a spoon tapping on a glass will work. Start from a distance and tap a few times very quietly, then ask your child to describe the sound and the reaction. Move a bit closer, and repeat. Practicing this regularly can help with the management of the overwhelm that may be felt. When one gets used to something, it becomes somewhat innocuous. Your end goal is to create a few different sounds to show your child that they are capable of managing audible sensory experiences.

Guided Meditation/Relaxation

Exactly the same as the parent version, but for short stints, followed by reports about the experience.

Conscious Breathing

Technically, you can't see yourself breathing, but you can do exercises like holding a tissue close to your child's mouth and asking them to observe the motion of the tissue as they breathe out, followed by the calming motion as they breathe in. Benefits include improved hand-eye coordination, motor skills, and fun!

Mindful Walking

Go on observational walks with your autistic child. Encourage him or her to look at the colors of the trees and flowers, listen to the birds chirping, take in the smells, and report back. Implementation of your own mindful morning routine can also be taught, within the rules that your child observes, of course.

Staying in Control

Children can be manipulative, and they will pounce on any opportunity to take control away from their parents. However, as long as your child or children know that you are in charge, parenting is ever so slightly easier.

Adapting to New Routines and Using Schedules

Routine is good for children, whether they are neurodiverse or neurotypical, but the latter are better at adapting to new routines. It is a good idea to mix up routines, even if the adjustment is slight. Getting a whiteboard with markers and writing out a daily schedule is a great exercise. Perhaps you and your child would like to plan a two-day schedule and write it on the whiteboard together. Well, in advance of day two, you can introduce a very small change. For instance, if your family takes a mindful walk at 4 p.m. every day, move it to 4.30 p.m., and after dinner on the evening of day one, explain that the routine on day two will change. Rub out the 4 p.m. walk and replace it with the 4.30 p.m. walk. This is slow preparation for bigger changes, such as taking on a new type of therapy or going on an unplanned trip to the beach. Try to keep last-minute schedule changes to a minimum. Autistic children like a plan, so introduce small adjustments as a start.

Reward Good Behavior and Build Self-Esteem

Use positive praise to reinforce attempts, not results: "You worked really hard on that" or "You were able to figure that out even though it was difficult." If we can accept that we are insufficient in certain areas but still choose to like ourselves, then we are developing self-esteem. Successful interactions in terms of words, used positively, allow autistic children to grow their self-esteem. It is important to build a child's belief that they can handle their life and handle it well.

Make Your Home a Safety Zone

You don't want to have blinding lights or ranges of powerful colors, nor an environment that is too busy. Dim but pleasant lighting and the use of natural light where possible augur well for a comfortable and safe environment, which should be the case at home. The same applies to sound: Have the TV at a reasonable level, tell your child when you are going to fire up the washing machine, and allow some distance from the sound. Specify that homework must be done at table X and that eating must be done at the Y table. Keep pens, pencils, glue sticks, scissors, and other homework tools in the same place, preferably labeled. Keep dangerous items, like sharp knives, out of reach. Do the same with cleaning products that contain chemicals and with anything else that may cause harm. This is quite a logical one. Teach stranger danger and stress that your child, autistic or otherwise, must not open the door for someone they don't know. Rather be safe than sorry on all of the above aspects.

Nonverbal Observation

As we get to know someone better, we learn what a certain look means, what a gesture is telling us, what their eyes are saying, or how a nod is a signal for something.

Facial Expressions and Gestures of Autistic Children

As a parent or educator, you need to identify gestures and facial expressions that a child may use to indicate tiredness, hunger, or discomfort. Achieving this shouldn't be too hard, considering that parents generally get to know their child from birth and through the different stages thereafter.

Identifying Reasons for Tantrums

Obviously, a tantrum is not a silent occurrence, but it doesn't involve cogent verbal communication. Just like expressions and gestures, parents of autistic children will learn why their child has tantrums. Don't think for one second that neurotypical children don't have tantrums, but do think that the reasons may be different.

Pay Attention to Sensory Activities

As a parent, you will know how your child reacts, maybe scrunching up their eyes, covering their ears, or fiddling with their hands. It is more than just knowing how your child reacts; you need to be continuously observant, especially when entering an environment that may cause sensory overload.

Living in the Present

Mindset is vital; let me repeat! You will have to make adjustments and adaptations. You will have stress, and there will be tough times. However, you have the ability to be as kind to yourself as you are to your autistic child. Practice mindfulness, and teach mindfulness to your child or children. Plan a few days ahead in terms of scheduling, but learn to live in the present.

Chapter 8:

The Future Is Possible

The title of the previous chapter and the final sign-off paragraph are "living in the present." If we leave the past behind and live in the present, then the future is most certainly possible.

Unique Personalities in General

We can draw comparisons and extract similarities in personality or personality type, but no two personalities are the same. Opposites do attract, as they say, and sometimes they do, but often you and your best friend have incredibly similar traits that you express through your quirks. We tend to group types of people together, but groups overlap, and the wonderful thing is that we do not need to fit into a specific group.

Unique Personalities Specific to Autistic Individuals

Some people may dismiss autistic people as all being the same, and it does happen. As a parent of an autistic child, you will know that this is a ridiculous assertion. That is akin to saying that all asthmatics are the same or that all diabetics are the same. Similar traits exist but think about our associations and friendships. Take reading, for instance. You may be part of a book club, and that is the common interest, so you identify with the other members. However, you don't all need to like the same books. A good way to look at it is in a very broad sense, and I will continue with the book club example. Millions upon millions of people enjoy reading, but a smaller group prefers nonfiction; within nonfiction, some like self-help, others like biographies; you get the picture.

Autistic individuals tend to show signs of introversion, but so does half the world; thus, introversion is a broad category, but within introversion, you get different types of introverts. It could be argued that autistic individuals show more similarities than differences, but that is very debatable, and even if that is the case, it doesn't matter.

Anxiety Prone

To label autistic individuals as more likely to experience anxiety is not really putting those individuals in a box because it is the neurological part that conjures the similarity. People that have depression or PTSD, for instance, are prone to anxiety, and bearing in mind that sensory experiences bring on anxiety in autistic children, anxiety is not a personality trait, just like depression is not a personality trait.

Perceived Social Aloofness

Social aloofness is perhaps slightly closer to being a personality trait, but I am cautious about putting it in that category, largely because it is a neurotypical perception that is most often wrong. It is not a case of being disinterested in interacting socially, as opposed to the difficulty of overcoming the stress involved. In life, some people are just aloof and think that they are too good for the rest of us—a trait indeed of a narcissist. The big difference is that aloofness is part of a narcissistic personality, whereas an autistic individual is mistaken for being aloof by others.

Persistence

Being persistent is probably the closest aspect of a personality representation. To bring ADHD, a common trait is the inability to finish tasks or the abandonment of tasks when the person does not know what to do. Autistic children experience frustration differently, but not that differently. A neurotypical can be prone to getting frustrated and stressed out by failing to do something that doesn't appear difficult. Trying to learn how to play the piano is difficult, and people with low patience will undoubtedly struggle. Is low patience a personality trait, though? I'm reluctant to answer my own question because a lack of patience may be reframed as a problem with persistence.

The Personality Trait Model

Referred to as the "Big Five" personality trait model, this categorization of personality traits is most definitely a refined model compared with historical models. If we go back to the early twentieth century, there was a psychologist by the name of Gordon Allport who created a model defining 4504 different personality traits (Cherry, 2020).

Jump forward to 1947 and a book called Dimensions of Personality, written by Hans Eysenck, which theorizes that there are two dimensions: extraversion and neuroticism. In the late 1970s, he added psychoticism to complete the trifecta (Team, 2011). In more modern times, extensive research has produced what is widely recognized as the foremost model, i.e., the Big Five (Cherry, 2020).

Each part of the model is broken down into "high" and "low." The former means that a particular person is at the top of the scale in terms of emotion, whereas the latter refers to someone near the bottom.

Openness

A broad range of interests and inquisitiveness about other people, places, and things fall into the high category. On the low end, the hypothetical person is averse to change, lacks imagination, and is unlikely to want to step outside their comfort zone.

Conscientiousness

The highly conscientious individual is very attentive to the smallest of details, likes to have a set plan and/or schedule, and attends to important tasks first and, most often, immediately. At the bottom is the type of person who procrastinates, struggles to complete tasks, can't stick to schedules, behaves recklessly, and does not look after things.

Extraversion

As we probably already know, an extrovert is very open to meeting new people, striking up conversations with strangers, and maintaining high energy levels, often feeding off the energy of others. This type of person will generally have a large group of friends and will enjoy being the center of attention. It goes without saying that an extrovert is on the high side of this category. At the bottom of the scale is, of course, the introvert, who does not crave attention, is happier on their own, and finds socializing exhausting.

Agreeableness

On the plus side, we find people who display kindness and have a genuine interest in helping others that require assistance. Often, these attributes are accompanied by empathy and concern. The low part here is the kind of person that you want to avoid. They don't care about others, are quick to throw out insults, and are particularly skilled in manipulation.

Neuroticism

At the top end, people get upset quite easily. They display high levels of stress and find it difficult to recover quickly from a particularly stressful event. Anxiety and excessive worry tend to be present, which lend themselves to fast changes in mood. Being low in terms of this trait involves the ability to relax easily, dispel worrisome events, and get over setbacks very quickly.

What Now?

Understanding these personality traits can assist us in identifying the parts of our personalities that we don't like and wish to change. The same applies to helping your autistic child do the same thing. There are positives and negatives to each of the Big Five, depending on whether you fit into the low or high category according to each trait.

Some of the positives

- Being respectful

- Displaying friendly behavior

- Considering the feelings of others before acting

- Showing humility

- Cooperating as opposed to seeking out conflict or argument

- Always exercising objectivity

Some of the negatives

- Intolerance towards others and dismissive of their opinions

- Selfishness

- Being overly judgmental, especially when you display the same characteristics

- Lacking reliability

- Openly behaving in an arrogant manner

Self-Insight

The American Psychological Association (APA), Dictionary of Psychology, defines *self-insight* as:

"Understanding oneself in some depth—it is the mediate goal or the desired outcome of many types of psychotherapy."

Like parts of one's disposition or personality, self-insight needs to be worked on. It is hard enough to accept ourselves as we are, let alone gain a deep understanding of ourselves.

Self-Insight vs. Self-Awareness

Self-insight is the "why," and self-awareness is the "what" and the "how." The former refers to understanding why you act in the way that you do and why you think in the manner that you do. Furthermore, self-insight dictates whether or not one must continue acting and thinking in certain ways or whether changes need to be implemented. The latter knows what you do, and how you think and the effect that these actions and thoughts have on others.

The Theory of Mind

The theory deals with understanding the minds of others, what is going on in their heads, and essentially what they are thinking. We obviously learn more about the way people act, react, and display feelings as we get to know them better. One could term it observational, but it is also automatic in a sense, given that the ability to understand actions, reactions, and feelings starts developing in children around the age of three.

In autistic children, the theory of mind is not as clear-cut as it is in neurotypicals. In 1984 and 1985, a British clinical psychologist by the name of Simon Baron-Cohen, with the help of German psychologist Uta Frith and Scottish psychologist Alan Leslie, came up with the false belief test, also called the Sally/Anne test. The premise is that a young girl puts a ball in a basket and goes out for a walk; her name is Sally. Another young girl by the name of Anne then takes the ball out of the basket and places it in a box before Sally returns from her walk. This is a simple scenario. However, many autistic children, when asked where Sally will "look" for the ball, answer that she will look in the box. It is important to remember that the question deals with looking, not finding. The more likely scenario is that Sally would look in the basket because that is where she left the ball, but that would be a false belief because she does not know that the ball has been moved. Autistic children struggle to identify that false belief.

In their studies and administration of the test, the three psychologists found that 20% of autistic children could identify the false belief, while the other 80% could not. The results are fascinating, but their simplicity tells us a lot about the perceived differences in autistic children.

Deficit

First of all, we should not be using the word "deficit" because something is not missing in the cognition of autistic children. One observation is that autistic individuals find that understanding or identifying figurative speech is quite difficult. Let's say, for instance, an autistic child stands on a sharp rock and cuts themselves. These things hurt, but when asked how they feel, through tears or clenched teeth, the answer may be that they are happy. It is a case of not being in touch with feelings and giving an answer that they feel is correct. The same may apply when they witness another child, a neurotypical, let's say, succumb to a cut from the rock. A present lack of understanding is at play, which is why the term "deficit" seems to have stuck.

Another difficulty comes into play when reading fiction. Generally, autistic individuals prefer facts, and exploring facts lends itself to answering the "why" question. In any event, children love that question. In a fictional book, one character may play a practical joke on another, and the autistic reader may wonder why Brian and Sue, hypothetically, were involved. This goes back to the chicken crossing the road joke and the literal manner in which an autistic child may interpret it before concluding that it is silly or nonsensical. A good exercise is to review real-life situations that your autistic child has encountered and guide them as to how they felt, followed by a lesson on why they felt that way. The idea is that the child will then be able to understand, or at the very least identify, what another person is thinking in a similar situation. As your child starts to answer the "why" question in his or her own mind, the so-called deficit evens out.

Impairment in Social Interaction

In terms of the theory of mind, the literal interpretation also goes to the heart of social interaction. The aloofness referred to earlier can present itself in social interactions when an autistic child just cannot understand a metaphor or the need for it. As before, routines are like a constant reassurance because the child knows what comes next, what comes after that, and so on. Social interaction sometimes comes without a plan. As an example, a bunch of kids agree to meet at the park on their bikes, then decide whether they will throw a ball around or play catch. This can be disconcerting for an autistic individual; he or she would prefer a specific plan, i.e., ride to the park, play catch, or ride home.

Impairment in Communication

Imagine if you knew what someone was talking about but found the conversation boring. In your own mind, you start thinking about what you would like to add to the discussion, and you read the verbal and nonverbal cues in order to choose the right time to speak. Autistic children often don't change topics tactfully and might just interrupt and move on to what they want to talk about. Interrupting is rude, but the autistic individual may not understand that because they struggle with interpreting what the other participant is thinking or even why they are talking about something so boring.

Restrictive Behavior

Within this category, we have repetition in a verbal and nonverbal sense. Repeating the same motions, sitting in the same chair, wearing the same clothes, and following the same general routine characterize behavior that can be restrictive. The same applies to eating only a few types of food, preferring very specific lighting, and repeating facts on their favorite topics. Stimming, as discussed previously, comes into play, in addition to hours of focus on one thing only. Their behaviors are not autism-specific; many neurotypicals display restrictive behavior, maybe not to the extent of their autistic peers, but it is still there.

Language Deficits

Many of us, probably all of us, sometimes forget mid-sentence what we are talking about or struggle to find the correct word, which is one of the reasons for using "ummm" and "like" to give us time to think. Autistic individuals experience this differently, and it can be a challenge to get the words out. Otherwise, there can be an overuse of words in the form of blurting out something that doesn't make cognitive sense. Some autistic children develop the ability to speak at an older age than others, and some have limited language their whole lives. Neither is bad nor wrong; they just indicate in what areas more support is required.

Becoming a Human of Value

A whole bunch of humans go through life believing that they bring no value to society, but one could argue that a huge proportion of them are wrong. People recover from alcoholism, drug addiction, or gambling to regain their human value. It happens all the time, and value is different from person to person. Teachers add value, as do nurses, but housewives also add value. If you can make someone's life better by showing kindness, doing a favor, or helping a friend, you are adding more value than you might think. It doesn't matter if you are autistic or not. You don't have to invent something amazing, become famous, or get really rich. As a parent of an autistic child, you need to spread love, and when you receive that love back, you will know for sure that your child is adding value. Seeing your child's progress will make you proud of yourself and of your child.

Always remember what Winnie the Pooh said to Piglet when Piglet asked Winnie how to spell love:

"You don't spell it. You feel it."

Spreading love, even if it is unspoken, is becoming a human value.

Conclusion

I am sure you will agree with me when I say that the last eight chapters have been quite a ride! As parents, educators, autistic children or adults, brothers, and sisters, plus anyone else who has read the book, I hope that you have learned something, perhaps many somethings! I also hope that I have been able to change perceptions and dispel erroneous beliefs about autism. What follows is a brief recap that you can use to consolidate what you have read and, if need be, refer back to certain sections.

The term "neurodiverse" is an indicator that our brains operate in diverse ways. There is, however, a distinction between neurodiverse and neurotypical individuals. Not only does the former describe diversity in brain activity, but it also encompasses a range of mental illnesses. Autism and ADHD are not mental illnesses, and neurodivergent individuals are not sick, disabled, or have special needs. Autistic children and adults experience the world differently, that's all. The old-fashioned and offensive terms, as well as general language, need to be reformulated. As an example from chapter one, a child is autistic, not autism.

Explaining to children at a young age that they are autistic is highly encouraged, and in such cases, it has been shown that the quality of life is better as young autistic children grow up. Interestingly, gender differences play a role in the identification of autism in that autistic boys are easier to identify than autistic girls. Sadly, the stigma stretches across gender lines, but ongoing research and awareness are slowly making a dent in that stigma.

Sensory experiences are central to differences in processing between autistic and neurotypical children. You will remember the analysis of the eight senses and the manner in which hearing, for example, is somewhat of an assault on the ears. Similarly, what one would consider being comfortable lighting may be near-blinding for an autistic child. Furthermore, the vestibular system establishes differences in spatial awareness, balance, and coordination. These sensory challenges can be overwhelming and can create extreme stress and discomfort. In general, sensory processing has been shown to be challenging for neurodivergent individuals.

Self-regulation, which involves stimulatory behavior, is a defense tactic. Parents and educators can assist in developing these combat tactics in order to improve quality of life.

A point of parental awareness must be directed towards masking or camouflaging, which entails autistic individuals developing a persona according to the way in which they *think* they should act. We want autistic children to be themselves and maintain a sense of individual identity. Masking and camouflaging contribute to the late identification of autism, which makes it more difficult to ease the need for autistic children to hide their true selves.

The neurodivergent development of social skills is different, and due to no fault of their own, autistic children can have trouble communicating. Rudeness is often an unfounded perception among neurotypicals. However, due to the literal nature of autistic children, manners may appear to be lacking. Initiating conversations, especially with strangers, may be daunting, and the stress involved often contributes to not participating at all; otherwise, people avoid eye contact, often unknowingly, and miss social cues.

Friendships appear difficult to form, but explanations and different exercises can ease the difficulty. An excellent way to slowly introduce autistic children into "friend-making scenarios" is through sports. Like-mindedness and enjoyment of the same activities can be a kick-start to discussions. Autistic children tend to prefer individual sports involving other participants. Examples would be swimming, horseback riding, and martial arts.

We often hear the term "constructive criticism," which doesn't apply exactly to autistic children, but using words and sentences in a constructive way is of great use. It can be challenging to understand how autistic individuals function, but with awareness of schedules, routines, and stressors, that understanding can be broadened. It also helps to take note of the levels of autism and the corresponding support requirements, in addition to the differences between the medical and social models. In a sentence, the former indicates a disease or problem, whereas the latter describes social differences, not abnormalities.

Sadly, autistic individuals have shown a propensity for self-harm, and one of the reasons is that depression and chronic anxiety can be coupled with autism. Life expectancy in autistic people is not very high, and a contentious issue is the lack of willingness shown by medical insurance companies to assist financially. This is something that we can work at changing by spreading awareness and giving the autistic community, their families, and advocates a platform to have their voices heard.

We do try to stray away from the term "diagnosis," but for the sake of practicality, receiving one can evoke a spectrum of feelings. Some parents experience fear, others feel relief or perhaps regret, and often need to progress through the ASD grief cycle to find acceptance. The Holland and Beirut stories may have assisted you in putting things into perspective and facilitated a way of understanding and explaining what it is like to receive the diagnosis and go on with life thereafter. Your mindset may require adjustment, and living day by day can make parenting a little easier. Negativity is bound to creep in, but alleviating the associated stress and anxiety should be achieved by being kind to yourself. Your autistic child may struggle with self-care and need reminders to brush his or her teeth. For instance, as a parent, you need to take care of yourself by doing things you enjoy.

Mindfulness is something to look into. It is rooted in being present, focusing on the now, and distracting yourself from the stressful thoughts that are firing around in your brain. Mindfulness can also improve the quality of life for autistic children, and it can be done together.

Don't lose sight of the fact that you are working towards a world in which autistic children can display their unique personalities. Make it your goal to prove the theory of mind wrong, or at least to give your autistic child the tools to remove perceived deficits, and restrictive behavior and become socially comfortable. Show your autistic child what it means to be a person of value, and learn the same thing from them using the most powerful human connection tool, love.

I would like to leave you, the reader, with a quote by the highly respected autism advocate Temple Grandin:

"Your autistic child has unlimited potential, just like everyone else."

Don't forget that, and don't let your child forget that either.

References

Alexandra, W. (2021, September 27). *What does the autism puzzle piece mean?* https://www.autismtalkclub.com/what-does-the-autism-puzzle-piece-mean/

Autism and social impairment. (2021, June 30). Alliance ABA therapy. https://www.allianceabatherapy.com/blog/302845-autism-and-social-impairment

Autism Spectrum Disorder. (n.d.). American Psychological Association. https://www.apa.org/topics/autism-spectrum-disorder

Autism and diagnosis: Advice for teachers. (n.d.). Autism. https://www.autism.org.uk/advice-and-guidance/professional-practice/teachers-diagnosis

A Non-linear Look at the Stages of Grief. (2022, April 18). Hospice & Palliative Care. https://hospicechenango.org/a-non-linear-look-at-the-stages-of-grief/?gclid=Cj0KCQiAtbqdBhDvARIsAGYnXBNgX01pY1-DRCXYC1FMIGmwbBL2h4otF-69ZRCLwXYtMTsYBn4HaGsaAq_tEALw_wcB

Autism and Smell Sensitivity. (2022, August 10). Hidden Talent Saba. https://hiddentalentsaba.com/autism-and-smell-sensitivity/

Bachrach, S. (2016, September). *504 Education Plans.* Kids Health. https://kidshealth.org/en/parents/504-plans.html

Bernstein, J. (2021, December 26). *The 3 Challenges for Parents of Adult Children with autism.* Psychology Today. https://www.psychologytoday.com/intl/blog/liking-the-child-you-love/202112/the-3-challenges-parents-adult-children-autism

Brenner, J. (2021, August 26). *The Puzzle Piece Versus Infinity Symbol - What to Use to Represent autism?* Study Breaks.

https://studybreaks.com/thoughts/puzzle-piece-infinity-symbolas-a-symbol-for-autism/

Bruise, C. (2021, November 15). *What Does It Mean to Be Neurotypical?* Healthline. https://www.healthline.com/health/neurotypical

Bushra, F. (2019, December 9). *Self-Harm in Children and Adolescents: Attention Seeking or Cause for Concern?* ACAMH. https://www.acamh.org/blog/self-harm-in-children-and-adolescents-attention-seeking-or-cause-for-concern/.

Buonviri, N. (2017, August). *Successful AP Music Theory Instruction: A Case Study.* Researchgate. https://www.researchgate.net/publication/318863228_Successful_AP_Music_Theory_Instruction_A_Case_Study

Cachia, CL. (2017, April 12). *Mindfulness and Autism Spectrum Disorder.* Intechopen. https://www.intechopen.com/chapters/52480

Cage, E., Di Monaco, J., & Newell, V. (2017, October 25). *Experiences of Autism Acceptance and Mental Health in Autistic Adults.* NCBI. https://www.ncbi.nlm.nih.gov/pmc/articles/PMC5807490/

Cage, E., & Troxell-Whitman, Z. (2019, January 9). Understanding the Reasons, Contexts and Costs of Camouflaging for Autistic Adults. https://www.ncbi.nlm.nih.gov/pmc/articles/PMC6483965/

Cherry, K. (2020, September 23). *Gordon Allport's Impact on Psychology of the Personality.* Very Well Mind. https://www.verywellmind.com/gordon-allport-biography-2795508

Cookes-Campbell, A. (2022, July 27). *8 Social Skills Advantages: How Socializing Can Take You to the Top.* Betterup. https://www.betterup.com/blog/social-skills-examples

Cook, J., Crane, L., Hull, J., Bourne, L., & William, M. (2022, August 24). *Self-Reported Camouflaging Behaviours Used by Autistic Adults: A Summary for Non-Academics.* Reframing Autism. https://reframingautism.org.au/self-reported-camouflaging-behaviours-used-by-autistic-adults-a-summary-for-non-academics/

Croner, I. (2013, August 16). *Using Affirmations with Young Children.* Croneri. https://app.croneri.co.uk/feature-articles/using-affirmations-young-children#:~:text=Using%20affirmation%20cards%20with%20children,use%20in%20their%20own%20language

Danny, R. (n.d.) *Asperger Experts.* Linkedin. https://www.linkedin.com/in/danny-raede-49b578176.

Davis, K. (2012, unknown). *What Triggers Anxiety for an Individual with ASD?* Iidc. https://www.iidc.indiana.edu/irca/articles/what-triggers-anxiety-for-an-individual-with-asd.html

De Conceicao. (2017, March 29). *Autism and Diagnosis: Advice for teachers.* Autism. https://www.autism.org.uk/advice-and-guidance/professional-practice/teachers-diagnosis

Denworth, L. (2020, April 8). *How People with autism Forge Friendships.* Scientific American. https://www.scientificamerican.com/article/how-people-with-autism-forge-friendships/

Deweerdt, S. (2017, November 15). *In autism, Food Quirks Show Up in Social Brain Areas.* Spectrum News. https://www.spectrumnews.org/news/autism-food-quirks-show-social-brain-areas/

diGiambattista, C., Ventura, P., Trerotoli, P., Margari, F., & Margari, M. (2021, July 9). *Sex Differences in Autism Spectrum Disorder.* Frontiersin. https://www.frontiersin.org/articles/10.3389/fpsyt.2021.5398 35/full

8 Simple + Accessible Mindfulness Activities for autism. (2021, January 30). Yoremikids. https://www.yoremikids.com/news/mindfulness-for-autism

Ernsperger, L. (n.d.). *The 3 R"s for Bullying Prevention: Recognize, Respond, and Report.* Autism-society. https://www.autism-society.org/wp-content/uploads/2014/09/3-R%E2%80%99s-for-Bullying-Prevention-Recognize-Respond-and-Report.pdf

Eversole, M., Collins, D., Karmarker, A., Colton, L., Quinn, J., Karsbaek, R,. Johnson, J., Callier, N., & Hilton, C. (n.d.). *Leisure Activity Enjoyment of Children with autism Spectrum Disorders*. Pubmed. https://pubmed.ncbi.nlm.nih.gov/26210514/

Efficacy of occupational therapy using Ayres sensory integrative approach for children with developmental disabilities. (n.d.). Researchgate. https://www.researchgate.net/profile/Roscann-Schaaf/publication/321816139_Efficacy_of_Occupational_Th erapy_Using_Ayres_Sensory_Integration_R_A_Systematic_Re view/links/5a54fa7045851547b1bd5680/Efficacy-of-Occupational-Therapy-Using-Ayres-Sensory-Integration-R-A-Systematic-Review.pdf

Faye, C. (2022, May 12). *9 Ways to Celebrate World autism Day*. Blog - Stage Learning. https://blog.stageslearning.com/blog/9-ways-to-celebrate-world-autism-day

Glenwright, M., Scott, R., Bilevicius, E., Pronovost, M., & Hanlon-Dearman, A. (2021, July 02). *Children with autism spectrum disorder can attribute false beliefs in a spontaneous-response preferential-looking task*. Frontiersin. https://www.frontiersin.org/articles/10.3389/fcomm.2021.669 985/full

Guestblogger. (2021, March 31). *Neurodiversity & Neurodivergent: What do they mean and how do they impact me as a PGR?* University of Glasgow PGR Blog. https://uofgpgrblog.com/pgrblog/2021/3/24/neurodiversity

Garcia Winner, M. (n.d.). Social thinking. www.socialthinking.com/Speaker%20Details?name=Michelle+Garcia+Winner

Hall, J. Leary, M. (2020, September 17). *The U.S. Has an Empathy Deficit. Here's What We Can Do About It*. Scientific American. https://www.scientificamerican.com/article/the-us-has-an-empathy-deficit/

Harris, TJ. (n.d.). *Reducing Self-Stimulatory Behaviors in Individuals with autism*. May Institute. https://www.mayinstitute.org/news/acl/asd-

and-dd-adult-focused/reducing-self-stimulatory-behaviors-in-individuals-with-autism/

Hatch-Rasmussen, C. (n.d.). *Sensory Integration in autism Spectrum Disorder.* Autism. https://www.autism.org/sensory-integration/

Henderson, L. (2022, Unknown). *Autism, Autonomy, and Touch Avoidance.* Disability Studies Quaterly. https://dsq-sds.org/article/view/7714/7598#:~:text=Autistic%20children%20commonly%20avoid%20social,hyper%2D%20or%20hypo sensitivity%20of%20touch.

Htreasure. (2018, March 26). *Creating a safe environment for your child with autism: Hidden Treasures.* Hidden Treasures. https://htaba.com/creating-safe-environment-child-autism/

How to handle changes in routine with your child with autism. (2020, April 05). Behavior Options. https://behavioroptions.com/strategies-for-handling-adjustments-to-your-childs-routine/

Jack, C. (2020, June 2). *5 Reactions to a Diagnosis of autism Spectrum Disorder.* Psychologytoday. https://www.psychologytoday.com/us/blog/women-autism-spectrum-disorder/202006/5-reactions-diagnosis-autism-spectrum-disorder

Juillion, P. (n.d.). *What is the function of the hypothalamic pituitary adrenal HPA?* Study Buff. https://studybuff.com/what-is-the-function-of-the-hypothalamic-pituitary-adrenal-hpa/

Kalish, L. (n.d.). *What is Self-Regulation?* Your the Therapy Source. https://www.yourtherapysource.com/blog1/2020/01/19/what-is-self-regulation-2/

Kostelyk, S. (2019, September 23). *An Introduction to the 8 Sensory System.* Sensory processing explained. https://sensoryprocessingexplained.com/an-introduction-to-the-8-sensory-systems/

Laird, CT. (n.d.). *Real Life with Eustacia Cutler.* https://www.parentingspecialneeds.org/article/real-life-eustacia-cutler/

Lees, E. (2022, August 30). *Using Positive Language to Support Autistic Children.* Headteacher-update. https://www.headteacher-update.com/best-practice-article/using-positive-language-to-support-autistic-children-sen-special-needs-inclusion-schools-1/247470/

Lebow, HI. (2021, September 23). *All About Autistic Burnout*. Psych central. https://psychcentral.com/autism/autistic-burnout

Madell, R. (2019, April 1). *Battling the Stress of Living With Chronic Illness*. Healthline. https://www.healthline.com/health/depression/chronic-illness

Mantica, G. (2022, April 11). *The Power of Kindness in Improving Brain Health*. Neuro science news. https://neurosciencenews.com/kindness-brain-health-20360/

Marco, EJ., Hinkley, LBN., Hill, SS., & Nagarajan, SS. (2011, May). *Sensory Processing in autism: A Review of Neurophysiologic Findings*. NCBI. https://www.ncbi.nlm.nih.gov/pmc/articles/PMC3086654/

Marsh, E., & Heyworth, M. (2022, January 31). *Neurodiversity-affirming Language: A Letter to Your Child's Support Network*. Reframing Autism. https://reframingautism.org.au/neurodiversity-affirming-language-a-letter-to-your-childs-support-network/

Mayville, E. (2022, October 10). *Are There Differences Between Autistic Boys and Autistic Girls?* Psychcentral. https://psychcentral.com/autism/comparison-of-boys-and-girls-living-with-autism-spectrum-disorder

Meduri, A. (2017, November). *Autism Special Needs Checklist: Big Kids (Ages 6 - 12)*. Kids Health. https://kidshealth.org/en/parents/autism-checklist-bigkids.html

Mexia, J.P. (n.d.) *Navigating Depression with Mindfulness: A Guide to Incorporating Mindfulness Practices into Your Daily Life*. Elevate Your Mind Blog. https://elevateyourmind.blog/2023/01/18/navigating-depression-with-mindfulness-a-guide-to-incorporating-mindfulness-practices-into-your-daily-life/

Mills, D. (2016, April 1). *Why People with Autism Die at a Much Younger Age.* Healthline. https://www.healthline.com/health-news/why-people-with-autism-die-at-younger-age

Miranda, A., Mira, A., Berenguer, C., Rosello, B., & Baixauli. (2019, March 8). *Parenting Stress in Mothers of Children with autism without Intellectual Disability. Mediation of Behavioral Problems and Coping Strategies.* NCBI. https://www.ncbi.nlm.nih.gov/pmc/articles/PMC6418028/#:~:text=Studies%20have%20shown%20that%20more,mothers%20(Boyd%2C%202002).

Morin, A. (n.d.). *Sensory Seeking and Sensory Avoiding: What You Need to Know.* Judiadyer. https://juliadyer.com/sensory-integration/#:~:text=One%20of%20the%20 main%20 tasks,use%20of%20this%20sensory%20information.

Murray, D. (2017, May 22). *The Difference Between Knowledge and Skills.* G01. https://www.go1.com/blog/post-difference-knowledge-skills

NAPA Team. (2018, June 22). *How to Tame Your Sensory Seeker.* Napacenter. https://napacenter.org/how-to-tame-your-sensory-seeker/

Nazari, A. (2022, April 11). *Conversational skills in children with autism, how to improve them?* Luxia. https://luxai.com/blog/how-to-improve-conversational-skills-in-children-with-autism/

Neurodiversity-affirming language: A letter to your child's support network. (2022, December 05). Reframing Autism. https://reframingautism.org.au/neurodiversity-affirming-language-a-letter-to-your-childs-support-network/

Omahen, E. (2022, February 22). *Easy Ways to Help Your Child With Self-Regulation.* Autism Parenting Magazine. https://www.autismparentingmagazine.com/easy-ways-with-self-regulation/

Oredipe, T., Kofner, B., Riccio, A., Cage, E., Vincent, J., Kapp, S. K., Dwyer, P., & Gillespie-Lynch, K. (2022, February). Does learning you are autistic at a young age lead to better adult outcomes? A participatory exploration of the perspectives of

Autistic University Students. *Autism*, 136236132210867. https://doi.org/10.1177/13623613221086700

Phillips, M. (2022, September 7). *21 Sensory Toys and SPD Exercises for Your Sensitive Child.* https://www.additudemag.com/sensory-toys-spd-exercises-child/

Phung, J. Goldberg, W. (2019, June 25). *Promoting Executive Functioning in Children with Autism Spectrum Disorder Through Mixed Martial Arts Training.* Link Springer. https://link.springer.com/article/10.1007/s10803-019-04072-3

Porter, P. (2017, July 25). *Sensory Processing Disorder.* Sinetwork. https://sinetwork.org/subtype-3-sensory-discrimination-disorder/

Richey, B. (2022). *The autism Spectrum Disorder Grief Cycle.* Family Education. https://www.familyeducation.com/kids/neurodiversity/autism/autism-spectrum-disorder-grief-cycle

Roybal, B. (2020, December 4). *What is High-Functioning autism?* Webmd. https://www.webmd.com/brain/autism/high-functioning-autism#:~:text=%E2%80%9CHigh%2Dfunctioning%20autism%E2%80%9D%20isn,They%20can%20live%20independently.

Rudy, LJ. (2022, December 4). *What is the Difference Between High and Low-Functioning autism?* Very Well Health.

https://www.verywellhealth.com/high-and-low-functioning-autism-260599

Rzucidlo, S. (n.d.). *Welcome to Beirut.* Texas parent to parent. https://www.txp2p.org/Media/family-stories/Welcome_to_Beirut.pdf

Sensory Input. (n.d.). Apa Dictionary of Psychology. https://dictionary.apa.org/sensory-input

Self-Insight. (n.d.). Apa Dictionary of Psychology. https://dictionary.apa.org/self-insight

Stigma. (n.d.). The Britannica Dictionary. Retrieved December 13, 2022, from https://www.britannica.com/dictionary/stigma

Sander, V. (2022, March 29). *The 4 Levels of Friendship. (According to Science).* Social Self. https://socialself.com/blog/levels-friendship/

Sarris, M. (2022, April 5). *The Stigma of autism: When Everyone is Staring at You.* Spark for Autism. https://sparkforautism.org/discover_article/stigma-autism/

Scott, E. (2022, March 31). *How to Deal with Negative Emotions.* Very Well Mind. https://www.verywellmind.com/how-should-i-deal-with-negative-emotions-3144603

Seigler, A. (28 September 2022). *Puzzle Piece Is Hated by the Autistic Community: The History and What to Use Instead.* Fierce Auntie. www.fireceauntie.org/puzzle-piece-is-hated-by-the-autistic-community-the-history-and-what-to-use-instead

Shenoy, M.D., Indla, V., & Reddy, H. (2017) *Comprehensive management of autism: Current evidence, Indian journal of psychological medicine.* U.S.

National Library of Medicine. NCBI.
https://www.ncbi.nlm.nih.gov/pmc/articles/PMC5733418/

Smith, M., Segal, J., & Hutman, T. (n.d.). *Helping Your Child With autism Thrive.* Help Guide. https://www.helpguide.org/articles/autism-learning-disabilities/helping-your-child-with-autism-thrive.htm

Stanborough, J. (2021, November 19). *Autism Masking: To Blend or Not to Blend.* https://www.healthline.com/health/autism/autism-masking

Stasney, S. (n.d.). *The Way We Talk to Our Children Becomes Their Inner Voice.* This n that parenting. https://www.thisnthatparenting.com/the-way-we-talk-to-our-child/

Stevens, T. (2015, July 8). *Emma Ward is Painting Change for Children with Austism.* Courier Mail. https://www.couriermail.com.au/news/queensland/rockhampton/emma-ward-is-painting-change-for-children-with-autism/news-story/5661ac9924fc9171926f38c77133e52b

Swank, E. (2020, February 7). *What are Restricted & Repetitive Behaviors in autism.* Autism Assistant.

https://autismassistant.com/blog/125/what-are-autism-repetitive-behaviors

Stigma. (n.d.). The Britannica Dictionary. https://www.britannica.com/dictionary/stigma

7 Tips to Help Children With ASD Improve Eye Contact. (2021, December 1). Behavioral-innovations. https://behavioral-innovations.com/blog/children-with-asd-improve-eye-contact/

The stigma of autism: When everyone is staring at you. (2022, April 05). Spark for autism. https://wp.sparkforautism.org/stigma-autism/

Taylor, DJ. (2003). *Orwell: A (Brief) Life.* Orwell Foundation. https://www.orwellfoundation.com/the-orwell-foundation/orwell/biography/

Team, G. (2011, November 11). *Hans Eysenck (1916-1997).* Good Therapy. https://www.goodtherapy.org/famous-psychologists/hans-eysenck.html

Thorson, S. (2021, August 19). *About Ayres Sensory Integration.* Health Children. https://www.healthychildren.org/English/health-issues/conditions/developmental-disabilities/Pages/Sensory-Integration-Therapy.aspx

Uihak, SCC. (2020, July 1). *Visual Perception in Autism Spectrum Disorder: A Review of Neuroimaging Studies.* NCBI. https://www.ncbi.nlm.nih.gov/pmc/articles/PMC7350544/

Understanding the Different Types of Stimming. (2022, July 15). Experia. https://www.experia-usa.com/blog/understanding-different-types-stimming/

Visual Pathways. (n.d.). Richardsonthebrain. https://www.richardsonthebrain.com/visual-pathways

Villines, Z. (2021, November 28). *Everything to Know About Non-Verbal autism.* Medical news Today.

https://www.medicalnewstoday.com/articles/non-verbal-autism

What is Cognitive Behavioral Therapy? (2022, December 28). Arkview, Recovery. https://www.arkviewrecovery.com/rehab-blog/what-is-cognitive-behavioral-therapy-2/

Welcome to Holland - Interview with Author Emily Perl Holland. (2019, November 4). Cedarstory. https://www.cedarsstory.com/welcome-holland-interview-author-emily-perl-kingsley/

What is sensory integration? (n.d.) Sensory Intergration Education. https://www.sensoryintegrationeducation.com/pages/what-is-si

Wagner, D. (2016, June 27). *Polyvagal Theory in Practice.* Counceling. https://ct.counseling.org/2016/06/polyvagal-theory-practice/

Weathington, L. (2020, February 18). *Neurotypical vs Neurodivergent: What's the Difference?* Daivergent. https://daivergent.com/blog/neurotypical-vs-neurodivergent

Wheeler, M. (2020, October 1). *Guidelines for Parents on Addressing the Needs of Siblings.* Autism Spectrum News. https://autismspectrumnews.org/guidelines-for-parents-on-addressing-the-needs-of-siblings/

Wheeler, M. (n.d.). *Siblings perspectives: Some guidelines for parents.* IIDC. Retrieved https://www.iidc.indiana.edu/irca/articles/siblings-perspectives-some-guidelines-for-parents.html

Worsley, R. (2022, September 16). *Does Learning You are Autistic at an Early Age Lead to Better Adult Outcomes? A Summary for Non-academics.* Reframing Autism. https://reframingautism.org.au/does-learning-you-are-autistic-at-a-younger-age-lead-to-better-adult-outcomes-a-summary-for-non-academics/

Why do Autistic People Have Issues with Social Skills? (n.d.) Applied Behavior Analysis https://www.appliedbehavioranalysisedu.org/why-do-autistics-have-issues-with-social-skills/

What is Self-harm? (n.d.). Young Minds. https://www.youngminds.org.uk/young-person/my-feelings/self-harm/

Author Request

This is your opportunity to make a meaningful impact by spreading awareness!

"I am different, not less." - Temple Grandin.

At the beginning of this book, we discussed how using positive language can shape how children perceive themselves. This realization came from my personal experience of raising my own neurodivergent young adult daughter, and it was one of the main motivations behind writing this book.

If we are intelligent and well-meaning, we can learn from our own mistakes as well as from the mistakes of others if we pay attention. However, mistakes are not the only sources of guidance. We also learn by studying, observing, practicing, and sharing our experiences. As a reader, you now have the opportunity to contribute to the educational process of future generations.

Speaking up is a crucial action taken by many prominent advocates. For example, Eustacia Cutler advocated for her daughter, Temple Grandin, to be accepted and receive an education. Sadly, during the 1950s, the stigma surrounding autistic children often led many families to send them away.

Autism activists like Eustacia Cutler, and Temple Grandin have used their experiences and knowledge to help the next generation of autistic children lead extraordinary lives. While you may not have the same resources or time to advocate as Cutler and Grandin, you can still make a difference by helping other families overcome the stigma.

By leaving a review of this book, you can show other parents and educators how to communicate using neurodiversity-friendly language, thus breaking the stigma and fostering acceptance. Simply by sharing how this book has helped you and by telling readers what they can expect to find inside, you will guide them toward a more inclusive and understanding perspective on neurodiversity.

Thank you for your support. Your journey as a parent, student or teacher may involve further practical work, but this is an excellent starting point regardless of your chosen direction. Sharing our knowledge and experiences contributes to a more accepting society for neurodiverse individuals.

To leave a review, please scan the QR code below.

Made in the USA
Las Vegas, NV
26 September 2023

78072699R00085